To my dear Reg

As busy as he was with the Agena program putting men on the moon, he still found time to be a cofounder with Michele le Menestrel Ullrich of the original Friends of the Vieilles Maisons Françaises, now the French Heritage Society, and serve as Chairman of the Board all those years until 2000, when he became Chairman Emeritus as a consultant.

Acknowledgements

To everyone, especially my friend Ellen Pearson, who provided encouragement to me to keep writing, and in particular Gia Manry, whose editorial talent molded my stories into book form, and Linda Manry, who seemed to know just how to bring all the pieces together, I offer my heartfelt thanks.

A Note from the Author

I notice that many books state that "all characters in this book are fictional and any resemblance to persons living are purely coincidental," so I feel some explanation of my own practice is appropriate.

My stories begin with true events but of course, as a story teller, just the bare facts would not make a good story. So I have mixed people's names however they came to me, occasionally combining multiple people into one character or intentionally muddling their names.

One plus to writing a book at almost ninety years old is that there are very few people left to contradict my memories, and I hope my dabbling in fiction will keep those remaining content.

Fran Kearton

Best wishes
Frank

Table of Contents

Travels with Reg 9

The Don Juan of rue Vavin 19

The Silver Knife...27

Miss French Flair 39

18 Quai de Bourbon...51

The Colonel's Wife...69

The Gold Crown 83

Floating Down the Seine 91

Mr. Big-As-A-Lion 105

That Tugboat Couple..121

Sans Plomb 129

Bonne Chance...147

Plumbers and Pompiers...157

Mysterious Neighbors 167

The Princess and the Pea 177

A Weekend at Fontainebleau 183

Southern French..197

The Marseilles Mafia..203

Channel Crossing...217

By the Time We Get to Phoenix......................................227

Travels with Reg

On a rainy March 27th Saturday in 1954, Reginald Ruston Kearton, a Pennsylvania Yankee Aquarian, and Frances Peace Adams, a Southern Taurus, were married in the First Presbyterian Church on Peachtree Street in Atlanta, Georgia.

Each had a previous marriage but both had been single for a decade. Both had responsibilities to bring to the union other than to each other: Reg, with two teenage sons and his elderly parents; me, Fran, with a teenage son and a widowed mother. As Reg loved his mother, perhaps the fact that I shared the same April 24th birth date with her may have added to my appeal.

In spite of our late start, we managed for 49 years to avoid the War Between the States, known by some as the Civil War. I have never understood how the word civil could have two such disparate meanings, such as: civil, courteous, polite, well behaved, etc. The opposite definition of "warlike."

My son Allison once remarked that even when Reg and I argued, it was with warlike civility, so perhaps the two definitions can be combined.

This was never more evident than when Reg and I were in a car searching for a destination in France. Our love of France and the friends we made during our many stays there was a strong mutual tie.

When Reg began his visits to France on business for Lockheed Aircraft Missile and Space Corporation in California in the early sixties, France stole his heart. Even though his English father made him appreciate his British roots, France was his adopted country.

He loved it so much he eventually became a co-founder with others who joined Michele le Menestrel Ullrich's pioneer vision of the French-United States liaison. For over twenty-five years Reg served as Chairman of the now 17 chapters of the French Heritage Society, also known as the Friends of Vieilles Maisons Francaises.

The chapters support the restoration of French-related architectural gems both in the United States and France, along with sponsoring student exchange programs educating young people in rapidly disappearing restoration techniques for building, gardens, and art.

As for me, I inherited my interest in France from my mother, Margaret Brooks Peace, a French major and 1906 Vassar graduate. She exposed me to the history and language at an early age. Unfortunately, and to her disappointment, her daughter never became fluent in the beautiful language.

At the time of the Adams-Kearton marriage in '54, I had become interested in the study of astrology, which I kept to myself since most people probably thought it was a mysterious disease or worse, a satanic cult. Before such a major step as a wedding, I sent for an astrological compatibility chart. A few weeks after our wedding, the report came with this advice: "Do not marry this man. An Aquarian is too adventuresome and globally oriented for a Venus-ruled home-loving Taurus, who likes stability and dislikes surprises. You will not be happy with him."

Excuse me! So much for her interpretation. I didn't take that too-late advice seriously. Reg and I vowed we'd waited too long in between marriages to make another mistake. Our 49 years of marriage was made far more fascinating and interesting by our differences than if we had been Tweedledum and Tweedledee.

The nearest we thought of second divorces was during the long car drives in France or on the Paris Metro. Reg was a typical auto-route male and I was a typical female looking out of the car windows saying "Oh Reg, there's that famous chateau I'm dying to see coming up on the next turn off."

Reg whizzes by the turn off and asks, "I didn't hear you, what did you say?"

Never mind. We wouldn't have been lost so often if he had heard me. As he is usually the driver, I am the navigator. So I am following the *map*, for God's sake, when I say "Dear, on the next block coming up, make a right turn."

Reg says "No, we go left."

I reply: "Well, if we go left, the street dead-ends into the Seine and we will drown. Right will take us home to 34 Guynemer." By then I am screaming even though I know it's disconcerting to a man driving the Paris streets in a Citroen he is unfamiliar with and a cataract which he is.

"Okay, Fran, I'll follow your directions by turning RIGHT to prove you are WRONG."

He turns right, makes another turn, and we arrive at our newly rented Paris apartment at 34 Guynemer. I can't help it if my DNA includes a sense of direction and Reg has directional dyslexia. Intelligence has nothing to do with it. I don't understand Reg's fantastic knowledge of his work in putting astronauts on the moon, aerodynamics, missiles, and politics, to mention a few.

Yet I have one miniscule gene. I am at the top of the chart in getting from here to there with a map. Why does he feel his entire masculinity is challenged because of a talent that points me in the right direction without a compass, and it's not a bunny tail?

The aforementioned 34 Guynemer address was my favorite so far of all of our Paris rentals.

After six years of the Madame at 40 Georges Mandel (whom I had mentally labeled the callous "Madame Defarge" of Dickens' Tale of Two Cities fame), I expected the same mistreatment from Madame Fournet-Histin, our landlady owner in August of 1988.

In spite of the excellent location on Georges Mandel, Madame Defarge's salt was the seemingly trivial source of my rebellion. Year after year we left her apartment in better order than we found it. Each time we returned, the TV always needed repairing and half the furnishings remained covered with sheets with "ne touchez pas" notes pinned to them. The two glass-plated kitchen cupboards were still firmly locked so I could see but not use anything in them, including large cartons of salt and pepper. So I must again buy a carton of salt.

In contrast, our new landlady was pleasant and generous. I thought I was in another country. Madame Fournet welcomed us with flowers and wine on the table, and opened her kitchen cupboards to say "help yourself."

I appreciated the quiet apartment overlooking the Luxembourg Gardens. Marie de Medici may not have been a popular queen, but she certainly knew petunias when it came to gardens. I spent many pleasurable hours walking there and watching the children sail their boats, or sitting with them for the Punch and Judy puppet shows.

Also, we lucked into a safe street. Since a high-ranking member of the Cabinet lived in the building, we had a full-time police guard.

Therefore I was content to stay away from such popular attractions frequented by the thousands of August tourists as the Tour Eiffel, the American Express office across the street from the Opera House, and the Louvre.

The only time we ventured into their territory was one hot Sunday when Reg expressed a desire to see Mitterand's newly-unveiled glass Pyramide at the Louvre. I hesitated to put a damper on Reg's sudden interest in art for, as to my knowledge, he had never set foot in the Louvre.

At least he was honest about it. Once I suffered through a dreary dinner with a minor Washington bureaucrat who bragged that he had covered everything worth seeing in the Louvre in twenty minutes. Is there an Olympic category for such an accomplishment?

When I suggested perhaps a Sunday afternoon at the height of the tourist season, to say nothing of the bicentennial activities, was not the best time to plan such an excursion, Reg had a different opinion.

"Fran, remember the French leave Paris for the country in August?"

I sighed. "Reg, I think you have the Parisians confused with the tourists."

In spite of my warnings, we took the Metro and popped out at the Palais Royale station directly in front of the Louvre's courtside entrance into what was my idea of hell...a mass of humanity. Every visiting American, German, Indian, Middle Easterner, Far Easterner, and natives of countries I had never heard of were surging through, or trying to.

But once Reg gets his mind set on a project, there is no turning back. He grabbed my hand and pulled me along behind him. Somehow we got into the flow, passed the Pyramide, looked at the people in the courtyard lying beside or wading in the pool, and struggled through the crowd to the exit.

I fanned my face with my purse and said "Wow, we made it out alive. As long as we're near, let's walk down the rue de Rivoli past the Tuileries to see the exhibition for the bicentennial celebration."

While we were walking, we noticed that since our last visit, all those beautiful buildings DeGaulle had sandblasted clean are now covered with scrawling wormlike graffiti. It was as if some strange alien fungus had covered everything, on the Metro stairs, walls, and even bridges. About the only thing that was impressive about the vandals (I can't agree with some who label them "graffiti artists") is their agility, as I saw scrawls in places that looked impossible to reach physically. And the evil spirits managed to obliterate bus line and Metro instructions, and even pay phone books.

By then we'd reached the Tuileries and stopped to stare in disbelief. Quelle surprise! The elegant garden was filled with the reproduction of a carnival midway such as I remembered as a child in Atlanta. The Lakewood Fairgrounds was the site of Georgia's annual State Fair for agricultural and livestock exhibits, with a carnival midway for entertainment. The hot dogs and cotton candy were consumed while enjoying such sideshow scientific features as Elwyn, the World's Strongest Man; Hector, half-man, half-turtle; and in a glass jar, the brain of Lennard Tutwiler, a mass murderer.

The French amaze me sometimes. How could a nation that gave the world Rodin, Van Gogh, Monet, Manet, the Eiffel Tower, and so many timeless contributions to civilized living in the world, suddenly have an air pocket in artistic judgment?

Mitterand didn't ask me, but to have people in period costumes strolling around the gardens, and even a tasteful guillotine at the entrance, representing a time in their history or a son et lumière would have been a better way to go.

Later we heard from friends who lived in an apartment on the rue de Rivoli facing the gardens that they woke up one morning and were greeted with the sight of a Ferris wheel installed across the street. That is why sensible French natives flee to their beautiful countryside in August.

I was later pleased to hear that the tawdry traveling midway was such a failure, it was abolished after a brief time.

Madame Fournet agreed to be our landlady once again the following year, so I was happy to think of going back to such a pleasant and now familiar environment.

The following French-related stories were written over a period of several years in no particular order, with no idea of a book. Like Topsy in Uncle Tom's Cabin, they "just grew."

Thank goodness I didn't take the astrologer's advice in 1954 seriously when she cautioned "do not marry this man, you will not be happy." My life with Reg broadened my horizons far beyond the confines of Atlanta, what was then a southern provincial city. These were wonderful years, the aircraft and astronaut space years, and the years in France, with a husband who may have been a headache, but was never a bore.

"Fran, remember the French leave Paris for the country in August?"

I sighed. "Reg, I think you have the Parisians confused with the tourists."

A few weeks after our wedding, the report came with this advice: "Do not marry this man. An Aquarian is too adventuresome and globally oriented for a Venus-ruled home-loving Taurus, who likes stability and dislikes surprises. You will not be happy with him."

Excuse me! So much for her interpretation.

Travels with Reg

The Don Juan of rue Vavin

When Madame Fournet turned over the keys to 34 Guynemer, she gave me a list of markets for daily living, such as the boulangerie, fresh produce, pharmacie, newsstand, and the boucherie, all located on the nearby rue Vavin.

From my former stays in France I'd learned that a daily visit to the boulangerie for bread is a must. Those mouth-watering loaves are baked early in the morning and must be eaten fresh. It doesn't take long for a loaf to become a hard, lethal weapon.

The boucherie was next to the boulangerie. And I was going to put off that challenge as long as possible.

I had never had luck with butchers, and doubted in this lifetime that I would find a friendly one. The first glance at my timid and undecided-looking face over their counter signals that here stands a woman who has no concept of which end of a cow comes first, the parts that are edible and the ones that need iron jaws to chew.

When Reg and I married in 1954, I had done no cooking since a decade ago, in a brief young marriage. And had forgotten the little I knew then. So, <u>The Joy of Cooking</u> stayed permanently open in our Atlanta kitchen. But the book assumed you only needed to know how you prepared the meat you had already bought.

When I asked my neighbor, married friend Alma Ross, for advice, Alma said "Fanny, Mr. Babb's meat market on Peachtree at Collier Road is the best. He's a dear man and handsome with his friendly smile and chubby pink cheeks. Tell him Mrs. Ross sent you."

Alma must have used more charm on Mr. Babb than I did because my first and only experience with the man was unforgettable as well as unforgivable.

One morning Reg told me that he had invited an Air Force Colonel and his wife for dinner. He suggested the Colonel's favorite was steak. Following Alma's advice to introduce myself to Mr. Babb, I asked him to give me the best steaks he had, which I guess he did in abundance. When Reg came home that evening, he found me sitting on the kitchen floor in front of the stove, weeping over a large half a cow, wondering how I could get it to fit in the oven.

I later learned that a filet mignon roast was what I should have ordered. Reg wiped my tears and returned the carcass to Mr. Babb, who refused to refund money. Instead he hung it in his freezer for our future consumption.

Too late for me to prepare dinner; instead we treated the Colonel and his wife to Atlanta's best steak restaurant.

As unreasonable as it sounds, Mr. Babb plus a few other unhappy experiences left me with a lasting negative, almost paranoid, opinion of the butcher's profession. And I didn't expect the French ones would be an improvement.

Therefore, after the first few days at 34 Guynemer, I'd patronized the baker, produce, and fish markets exclusively. The fish market stalls were open displays, and I didn't have to order anything complicated like different cuts of meat. Like a deaf mute, I would smile and point to a friendly-looking fish. The shop keeper wrapped it to hand it to a woman at the cash register. I'd ask "Combien?" and then pay the amount with no questions.

A knowledgeable French housewife said I might be paying for a whale instead of a small fish so I should check charges very carefully. Although fish is considered a very healthy diet, I also knew it would only be a matter of time before Reg would question the lack of variety.

That came the morning he said, "Fran, we have had nothing but seafood since we came here. How about a nice juicy steak tonight, or anything to keep me from growing gills?"

As Reg had no problem with timidity in any form, he would not understand my reluctance to tackle a new butcher in French when I'd had so little success in English.

My solution to the meat problem in the years of the Georges Mandel apartment was a supermarket in walking distance on the rue de Belles Feuilles off the Place de Mexique. But that location was many Metro stops from Guynemer.

Today, I determined to bravely walk into the Bourre boucherie to buy steaks. With a grocery list tucked into my pocket, I began walking towards the rue Vavin. After a few blocks passing only a small number of pedestrians, I heard a woman's voice behind me shouting "Madame, Madame, attendez, attendez!"

Turning around I saw a small gray-haired woman, waving her cane to point at me with one hand, and clutching a small object in the other. She limped towards me at a remarkably fast pace. I had no idea what I could have done to upset her since I'd never seen her before. I waited until the out-of-breath woman stood beside me before I learned the reason for her concern.

The object she was waving was my wallet.

Guardian angels come in many disguises, and this seemingly decrepit woman had seen me drop something from my basket, picked it up, and realized it was valuable.

I had put my combination wallet and change purse in my shopping basket. Perhaps on my way, while swinging the basket in time to my singing Ella Fitzgerald's hit song "A Tisket A Tasket, I Lost My Yellow Basket," the wallet had fallen onto the pavement.

She had returned most of my identity, all but my passport was in that wallet. I was so grateful, I wanted to give her a reward, but she would have none of that. Instead she followed me for another block to wag her finger and scold me for being so careless.

"Madame, toujours prenez garde. Il y a beaucoup de voleurs à Paris."

Before I could give her many more "milles mercies," she turned the other way and disappeared around the corner. Maybe she was Superwoman in disguise.

After that heart-thumping scare, I arrived at rue Vavin with no more incidents. List in hand, I stood looking into one of the front windows of the Bourrée boucherie for some time, composing my request. A filet mignon I knew was tender, as well as having a French name. Then I glimpsed my favorite, "un poulet rôti," in the other window. Reg would have to settle for chicken tonight—at least it wasn't fish.

By then I'd been standing at the entrance for so long, I'd attracted the attention of the young man behind the counter. He waved at me, cupped his hands around his mouth, and loudly said "Entrez, entrez!"

There were no other customers at the moment, so he introduced himself as Jean Bourrée, his mother at the cash register, and his father in the back room, hard at work.

"Mademoiselle, êtes -vous nouveau dans le voisinage? C'est vrai, bienvenue a Chez Bourrée."

This tall young man with the smiling eyes to match his killer smile had already made me aware in his first greeting of "Mademoiselle" instead of "Madame," here was an excellent salesman.

After I pointed to the chicken, he wrapped it while pointing to the trays of salads and plates du jours. I was hooked. This was better than any super marche. When he handed me the ticket to pay his mother at the cash register, he winked. I thought it might be an involuntary twitch, so I smiled and left the store.

That evening Reg was pleased to have something other than fish, and I promised him steak for the next night. I'd never have envisioned a time when I would look forward to going to a boucherie. But it helps, when one is in a foreign country, to have the natives friendly.

And friendly Jean Bourrée was. I learned the twitch was a genuine, first-class, flirty wink. I'm Southern and can't help it: he'd give me a wink and I would smile and wink right back.

The Bourrée store was usually crowded and once, when I decided at the entrance that there were too many people ahead of me, Jean waved and held up his hand in a thumb and forefinger gesture to say "Madame Kearton, votre ordre est à la caisse" Since I had not ordered anything, I followed his instructions and paid for the mystery package.

That evening, Reg said his filet mignon steak was the best ever.

The day before we left 34 Guynemer, I bought my final purchase from Jean. After all those weeks of winking and smiling, when Jean wrapped my four slices of ham, we finally had our Magic Moment. As he handed me the package, instead of a wink, he gave my hand a long, slow, and unmistakably tender squeeze before relinquishing the package.

Eat your heart out, Mr. Peachtree Street Atlanta Georgia butcher Babb. Probably Jean Bourrée is known as the Don Juan of rue Vavin. If he gives those squeezes and winks to all his mature lady customers, no wonder the shop's so popular. Nevertheless, I'm grateful to a gallant Frenchman for curing me of my secret fear of meat cutters.

This tall young man with the smiling eyes to match his killer smile had already made me aware in his first greeting of Mademoiselle instead of Madame, here was an excellent salesman.

"I appreciated the quiet apartment overlooking the Luxembourg Gardens. Marie de Medici may not have been a popular queen, but she certainly knew petunias."

The Silver Knife

One hot August afternoon in '89, I entered a Paris Metro car. With the exception of a lone woman, the car was eerily empty. I sank into a seat several rows behind her with a grateful sigh. At last I could relieve my aching arms by placing my large filled-to-overflowing basket on the space beside me. That same straw market basket, which had seemed so light when I'd closed the door of our rented apartment in the Sixth Arrondissement at the start of my journey, had turned into an albatross for the trip home.

The purpose of the long trip across to the Sixteenth Arrondissement on the Right Bank was to buy a few extra knives, forks, and spoons at a supermarket. Instead of sticking to my original goal, I'd greedily jammed more needed items in my basket than I could comfortably carry, including a ham which surely must have had piglets by now.

In an attempt to alleviate the problem, I'd spent a miserable quarter of an hour hailing taxi drivers. The speed with which they raced by made me wonder if this blonde woman standing on the sidewalk waving her arms and yelling "TAXI!" had "invisible" stamped on her forehead.

My hopes rose when one driver slammed on his brakes in a rough stop and asked me where I wanted to go. He shook his head when I gave him the rue de Guynemer address, which borders the Luxembourg gardens.

"Pas de Jardin," he said, with a jerk of his thumb in the opposite direction. "Le déjeuner," which indicated that he was on his way home for the long lunch. From the look of his balloon of a stomach, I was tempted to say that he could have afforded to skip a lunch or two to take me home, but one doesn't argue strenuously with Paris taxi drivers.

I gave up the struggle and staggered two more blocks to the Trocadero Metro Station. At least the underground was cooler than a taxi. I took advantage of the momentary privacy of the car to hold my wet, sticky blouse away from my body in order to reach inside and dry myself.

Although I grew up in Atlanta, Georgia, during times when air conditioning was as scarce as it still is in Paris, the sizzling heat of the past few days seemed more intense than any I'd felt in Georgia.

One more hurdle before home base—the change from Line Six to Line Nine at Pasteur Station. This had been a difficult trip for a few pieces of cheap flatware.

This morning's conversation with Reg had prompted my visit to a supermarket off la place de Mexico where I'd shopped often in years past.

"Fran, Jean Delachair flies in from Nice tomorrow…we've got a lot of business to do. Is it okay if he parks in the guest room for a couple of days?"

"'Course it's okay…I'm crazy about Jean…only we'll either have to eat in shifts here, or go out."

"For heaven's sake, why?"

"The only silverware Madame left out were the two place settings she laid for us on the dining room table…very dear of her with the flowers and all, but she never told me where the rest of it was."

"Probably thought we'd take it back home to California."

"No, no, this Madame isn't a bit like the last Madame Defarge…she just plain forgot to leave the key to that Bluebeard's hall closet."

"Well, go buy some more around the corner…that's easy. I'd do it myself but I've got to be out all day."

I sighed and thought to myself that it wouldn't be easy at all. To shop in an unfamiliar neighborhood in a strange country wasn't in the same league as a pop-in to my California supermarket.

The thoughts of supermarkets convinced me that it would take less time to visit my old haunt in the Sixteenth than it would to tackle the small shops around us with their hovering proprietors and no self-service. I knew exactly where my former market kept their array of kitchen utensils and flatware.

Also, a Metro trip would be easier than attempting a phone call for a cab. We were off the beaten track for cabs, and so far had little success with understanding the dispatcher's rapid-fire

French which filtered through the radio static. She was either telling us one was on the way, or one was not.

After washing the breakfast dishes in the sink, I chose my outfit for the journey across town carefully—a navy blue cotton skirt, a white blouse, and a red neck scarf plus the de rigueur market basket. When I surveyed myself in Madame's old-fashioned oval standing mirror, I was satisfied that I blended in well with the other woman shoppers on the street.

Maybe my efforts to look more like a French woman than a tourist was the reason I was often the target of questions from strangers. In Beirut or Tokyo, I could never pass for a native, but in France, it was a rare day when someone didn't ask me "Ou est le Metro?" or where was some particular street.

If the question was an easy one, I'd reach for the always present loaf of bread in my basket and point in the right direction. If I didn't know, I'd give the Gallic shrug.

The two items which gave me away in my masquerade before I opened my mouth to speak were my comfortable walking shoes and my sun hat. I was the despair of my long-time French friend Michele, whose continuous efforts to turn me into a clone of herself—an elegant French woman—sometimes met with Yankee stubbornness, or in my case, Southern balkiness.

The first time she saw my thick, rubber-soled navy clodhoppers, she threw her hands in horror and said "ooh la la, Françoise, only an American woman would dare wear such ugly shoes."

I refrained from mentioning that "those ugly shoes" saved my feet from turning into something uglier—the misshapen toes and bunions that many French women must have, caused by wearing too-small fashionable shoes on all occasions.

Another bone of contention with Michele was my insistence upon using a cabas à roulettes, those wonderful sacks on wheels, for shopping.

"Only a femme de chambre uses those," she wailed. "You'll disgrace me!"

"Better thee than me…they save me from a permanent stoop and a twisted spine from lugging heavy market baskets…besides, you *have* a maid. I *am* the maid here."

Unfortunately, the trusty wheeled cart was useless on the Metro, so it would stay in the kitchen on this trip.

After I'd dressed, made a list, pored over the red Taride Street and Metro Guide, transferred franc notes into a small change purse (a bulky hand bag was too tempting to the gypsy thieves who prey on Metro passengers), and set Madame's intricate burglar alarm, I'd taken over an hour to prepare for a simple crosstown errand.

Now my mission was accomplished and I was near the end of my journey. The main objective to my supermarket visit, the extra sets of stainless steel knives, forks, and spoons, was nestling in my basket on top of all the things I hadn't meant to buy.

When I got off at rue Notre Dame des Champs (which, incidentally, is the street where Hemingway lived during his Paris years), I headed for a bench in the triangular oasis near the Metro exit, one of the many small parks sprinkled throughout this civilized city.

During the times I'd passed the Park, the eight benches were usually occupied by elderly black-clad women feeding the pigeons, a couple of clochards—a softer word for *bums* than ours—and a scattering of students from L'Ecole des Beaux-Arts and other various schools in the section. The Sixth has been a mecca for writers, artists, and students for decades. There are more antique book sellers, printers, book binders, and publishers in the Sixth than there are bakeries.

Today the park was as strangely vacant as the Metro car had been. Apparently only mad dogs, Englishmen, and American women in search of supermarkets go out in Coward's noonday sun.

I fished around in my skirt pocket, found a tissue to wipe the pigeon droppings off the nearest bench, and sat down. I'd rest a few moments before kicking that infernal basket inch by inch for the few blocks home.

The heat and the sensation of being in this hidden corner of Paris surrounded only by old stones and such resident shades as Voltaire, Racine, and Gide lulled me into a dreamlike state.

Finally, a trickle of perspiration down my forehead triggered some action on my part. I grabbed my basket and marveled at how it had doubled in weight while lying on the ground. Out of the corner of my eye, I idly noticed a lone couple riding up on the Metro escalator. The middle-aged woman dragged her male companion behind her and headed in my direction. At the same time she clutched the man by the hand, she gestured with the other and cried, "Madame, Madame, aidez-moi."

She was in such haste that she trampled the red canna hedge which bordered the park instead of using the walkway. By the time I realized that I was the only *Madame* in sight, the couple stood in front of me. Uh-oh, I thought, here we go. Once again I was destined to fill my ill-equipped role of Paris Information Bureau.

On closer inspection, I saw that the man was in great distress. The white handkerchief he held to his face was covered with blood and my first thought was that he had been attacked on the Metro.

The woman explained, "Madame, mon pauvre mari, le nez, le nez, il a le saignement de nez."

Since the blood was still gushing from his nose onto his blue shirt and then to the ground, I had no trouble grasping the fact that the man did indeed have a nosebleed, but I had no idea what the woman wanted me to do about it. At that moment I longed for some of the elderly pigeon-feeding habitués of the park.

Suddenly, a surefire cure for nosebleeds came to mind. As a child in Atlanta, I had been prone to nosebleeds. My mother always stopped them by placing a cold silver knife along the back of my neck.

A knife, I needed a knife. Immediately I searched in my basket for one of my recent purchases, a stainless steel knife. Mother never specified that the knife *had* to be silver.

"Attendez, Madame, I'll help you." I pulled out the knife and with a triumphant flourish said "Voila, the cure!"

When the woman saw the knife she shrieked. I came to my senses and realized that not only had I frightened her, but that if I took my time to explain my mother's remedy for nosebleeds in my halting French, the man could bleed to death.

When she saw it was only a harmless table knife, she interpreted my action to mean that I thought she was looking for a surgeon. She said that she didn't want his nose removed, just a doctor who'd stop the bleeding.

Ever helpful, I said, "I know la pharmacie," and pointed towards one a couple of blocks away on the Boulevard Raspail. Although the woman had already decided that she'd chosen a real loser in the information department, she seized on that idea with many thanks and hurried off with her husband in tow. I suspect that she felt as if she'd escaped a far more sinister fate at the hands of the Madwoman of the Notre Dame des Champs than coping with a simple nosebleed.

I returned to 34 Guynemer, soaked in the tub, and sat around in my birthday suit awhile. By the time Reg returned, he found me serene and composed.

"Okay, what'd you do all day besides try to keep cool?"

"I went to our old neighborhood supermarket, the one on rue des Belles Feuilles…'cause I knew they had some cheap tableware. Now we don't have to eat with our fingers when Jean visits."

"That shouldn't have taken all day…what else did you do?"

"You know the escalator that comes up from the Notre Dame des Champs Metro? Well, this woman and man came off of it while I was sitting on a bench in that little park near there…the man had a nosebleed and the woman asked me for help…I tried to tell her about a wonderful cure Mother used on my nosebleeds…a silver knife held along the back of the neck…"

My audience had the same look on his face as the woman in the park.

"Fran, that remedy has no scientific validity whatsoever…it's a wonder the woman didn't think you were nuts."

"Believe me, she did…but it works."

Reg continued to shake his head. It was as difficult to explain a surefire Southern home remedy for nosebleeds to a Pennsylvania Yankee as it was to a French woman. Neither of them understood Southern English or French.

I gave a mental Gallic shrug to both of them.

Another bone of contention with Michele [Pictured, Center] *was my insistence upon using a* cabas à roulettes, *those wonderful sacks on wheels, for shopping.*

Georges Blanc

Etape de charme au cœur de la Bresse gourmande et au bord de la Veyle dans le magnifique domaine fleuri de Georges Blanc

Georges Blanc welcomes you in his superb flowered estate, a delightful stopover in the heart of gourmand Bresse on the banks of the Veyle

On this breezy April day, we'd been on the road for an hour before the thought of the treasure I'd left in the Georges Blanc hotel room there caused my outburst

37

Miss French Flair

Miss French Flair

"Reg, stop, stop!" I began hitting my hand on my forehead in frustration, "Look for a place to turn around; we have to go back to the hotel."

My husband looked suitably startled at this unexpected command and said, "Fran, are you crazy? If we waste any more time, we'll run smack into the worst traffic hours in Paris…and for what?"

Reg and I were returning to our rented Paris apartment from a weekend excursion in the movie-set village of Vonnas. On this breezy April day, we'd been on the road for an hour before the thought of the treasure I'd left in the Georges Blanc hotel room there caused my outburst.

I was almost in tears when I said, "Damn, damn. How could I have been so stupid? I've left my beautiful Irish wool coat in that small closet by the door."

Reg kept on driving as he said, "What coat? Oh, that funny colored one. Fran, be reasonable, too far to drive back...we'll call when we get to Paris."

"No, no, we have to get it *now*. Reg, it'd break my heart to lose my lucky Miss French Flair coat. Remember, it was one of the contest prizes?"

"How could I forget? The minute you walked out of the Alliance Française with the crown still hot on your head, the IRS sent me a notice reminding me I owed tax on your winnings....cheaper to have bought all that loot!"

"You don't mean that. It's your corporate accounting mind speaking. Your best friend Dale said you bragged about my winning that title for years. It's the English in you! An Englishman is noted for being less that generous with compliments to his wife, but tells his best friend how wonderful she is—so sometimes the wife elopes with the best friend. Then the mystified husband asks, 'Why?'"

"Hah, I can't see you running off with Dale any time soon. You can't stand him and you know how tickled I was over your triumph...if for no other reason than it helped you get over your depression."

In May of 1960 I won the title of Miss French Flair of San Francisco, which is somewhat ironic considering I'd recently moved to the Bay Area from my native Deep South. The Guinness Book of Records has no category for the "least-known contest title," otherwise mine would be in the running with such titles as Miss Cranberry Bogs, Miss Oregon Winesap, and other such regional Chamber of Commerce promotions.

Nevertheless, I couldn't have been more thrilled if I'd been crowned Miss Universe. At the time I was such a homesick little piece of southern-fried chicken that the morale booster prevented me from hightailing it back to Atlanta.

My entry into the contest happened by chance. A few months after our move West, I stopped by the cosmetic department in the City of Paris, an elegant store on San Francisco's Union Square, which is no more. After a few purchases from Simone, an attractive young woman clerk, mutual southern and French sociability meshed, so by the time she'd rung up my sale, we'd developed a dialogue.

After she'd suggested I fill out the French Flair contest entry form the store was promoting, Simone confided that she was a native Parisian and her husband's employer had recently transferred him to San Francisco.

When we compared homesick badges, I said she was the winner. At least I'd stayed in the same country, but often it didn't seem that way. Westerners were as strange to me as if the Lockheed Corporation had transferred us to Pakistan.

For starters, in the late fifties, few of the Westerners I'd met had ever visited the South, except for rare business trips. They traveled to Europe, New York, the Islands, and other exotic places. In fact, some of the men who'd been in the service had such unhappy memories of the Southern training camps they seemed to blame me for the suffering they'd endured from heat, snake bites, sadistic training procedures, and boredom.

My native Atlanta was far from the sophisticated New York of the South that it's known as today. Although it was Georgia's capital, the middle-size city had a low profile and wasn't known to the outside world for much more than the home of the ubiquitous Coca-Cola Company; Margaret Mitchell, author of Gone with the Wind; and the Grand Slam golfer, Bobby Jones.

As a newcomer, most of the people I met were a bit fuzzy on the subject of southern state geography. I became weary of some ham-handed well-intentioned host at a party introducing me by saying, "Here's a real southern belle. Meet this little lady from Louisiana, or was it Alabama, dear?"

I would patiently explain that I was a native Georgian and that any Georgian would rather confess to armed robbery than admit to being from Alabama. My statements that Georgia was one of the original thirteen colonies, and in Atlanta, we wore shoes, had a ballet company, a symphony and lots of trees, were met with ill-concealed disbelief.

Furthermore, unlike Hollywood's stereotyped dialogue writers who indiscriminately sprinkled "You-alls" like dandelion seeds throughout any southern script, southerners do not use it in the singular. "Y'all" means exactly that, all you plural people, not one person. My attempts to educate failed because hosts continued to greet me with, "Here's Miss Magnolia, how are you all, honey?"

Unfortunately the novelist Erskine Caldwell's unfavorable depiction of the South in "Tobacco Road" had planted too firm a picture of a country peopled by barefooted rednecks to change many minds.

Never mind, my new title would certainly earn me a little more respect. Instead of the frivolous sobriquet of Miss Magnolia, I was now Miss French Flair of San Francisco. So, how do you like them apples?

Naturally, I couldn't wait to pepper my left-behind Atlanta friends with the write-up to prove that already I'd made the San Francisco Chronicle instead of the Atlanta Constitution.

Gallic Contest

FHE★   **PAGE 11**
Friday, May 6, 1960
San Francisco Chronicle

Peninsula Housewife Is Winner

By Evelyn Hannay
Fashion Editor

Mrs. Reginald R. Kearton, 38, of 145 Fair Oaks lane, Atherton, was named "Miss French Flair" last evening by a group of judges in the Coty-City of Paris contest, which culminated at a party at the French Club on Mason street.

Twenty runners-up, including 95-year-old Sarah Ann Tomlinson of 130 Palm avenue, San Francisco, attended the champagne reception for the final judging.

Jean Despres, vice president of Coty Parfums, was here from New York to make the presentation of the prizes—a round trip to Paris for two via Air France jet, a Lilly Dache flower turban, and a complete wardrobe from the City of Paris.

Earlier, at a luncheon of the Downtown Association at the Hotel St. Francis, M. Despres, acting for Le Comite du Grand Prix Americain, had presented Mayor George Christopher with medal, naming San Francisco the city with "the most French flair."

Frances Kearton is a housewife and artist interested in water-color painting. She has a 17-year-old son and has longed to visit Paris ever since kindergarten when she learned to sing French songs

JEAN DESPRES AND "MISS FRENCH FLAIR"
Mrs. Reginald R. Kearton of Atherton goes to Paris

with the reception last night. The search was for a woman "who has a certain quali- her on poise, appearance, personality and the essay she wrote on her applica-

43

As a result, the first person I heard from was Mary Hurt Kilpatrick. Mary Hurt and I had been fast friends since school days and I'd been maid-of-honor in her wedding to Martin Kilpatrick at age 18 and the next month, she'd returned the favor when I married my son's father and first husband, Allison Hoyle Adams. So I wasn't surprised that she was the first with a congratulatory call. Or so I thought. Nothing like long-time friends to keep the old head from ballooning to Macy's New Year's parade-size since the conversation went something like the following:

"Fanny, so good to hear your voice and you sound much more cheerful. Ever since you pulled up stakes and headed West, you've sounded like Miss Dismal."

"Mary Hurt, did you get the newspaper article I sent? It explains my mood change. I'm beginning to feel more at home here now."

"Oh, sure, something about being named Miss France…well, that's certainly a title you wouldn't win here in Atlanta. I don't think there're more than four or five French people in the whole city and that's counting mean ole Madame Groleau, our Seminary French teacher. You know she flunked me and said I should choose another language 'cause no way was I ever going to master French with my 'cracker' accent? How'd you manage to win something French when your accent wasn't much better? All I can say is that if they had to name a Georgia 'cracker' Miss French whatever, they must not have many French people out there either."

Since Mary Hurt had a justified reputation as Miss Motor Mouth, I knew if I didn't jump in before she could take another deep breath, this would be a one-sided conversation. I seized the moment by saying "I didn't have to speak any French to win."

I explained that the head of Coty Cosmetics, acting for *Le Comite du Grande Prix Américain*, came from New York to present

Mayor Christopher with a medal naming San Francisco the City with the Most French Flair. The search was for a woman "who has a certain quality that makes her remembered—simply a woman who symbolizes French flair."

"Fanny, if it cheered you up, I'm happy, but I read in the article that a 95-year-old woman, Sarah Tomlinson, was one of the runners-up, and I think it's tacky to be competing with an old woman."

In spite of my protests that 200 other women entered the contest, among them many top models in San Francisco, I'd upheld the honor of Southern womanhood, Mary Hurt remained unconvinced. Her final words were, "I think out of courtesy and sportsmanship, you should have given the title to the 95-year-old."

While I was mentally reviewing that memorable evening fifteen years ago in San Francisco, I still had my main project in mind here in France, to retrieve my cherished coat.

"Reg, you've missed a lot of good places to turn around."

"Listen, I have a better idea. We'll have lunch in Tourneys, and I'll call the hotel to be sure the coat's still there."

"Okay, but remember that's the only thing left of my prizes...the first class round-trip Air France tickets to Paris, the wardrobe of outfits and rest are all gone. Did I tell you that M. Despres from Coty's and M. Luc, the French Consul, invited me for dinner after the ceremony at the Fleur de Lys Restaurant? The maitre'd tried to check my fleur-de-lis crown, and Lilly Daché hatbox, but I wouldn't give them to him."

Reg said, "M. Luc, M. Luc, the Consul. Oh, I remember him. He visited Lockheed several times to talk about French aircraft companies with me…but he never mentioned having met my wife."

"The man probably didn't connect you with me at all. You weren't with me that evening. Remember, you were in Cape Canaveral on business."

I decided not to confide in Reg that the main reason I'd never forget the French Consul was his ear compliment. During the Fleur de Lys dinner, M. Luc and M. Desires had a spirited argument concerning my ears and my ankles. M. Luc said, "Françoise, you have beautiful ears."

Then M. Desires chimed in to say, "No, M. Luc, I beg to differ. Her ankles are more beautiful than her ears. She has French ankles."

At that point as pleased as I was about having parts of my anatomy being singled out for praise that had never before been noticed, I had mixed emotions. What about the rest of me?

On the other hand, if Frenchmen appreciated ears and ankles instead of the American male's preference for bosoms and bottoms which in my case were less than ample, maybe I was living in the wrong country.

In my entire life, no one except Dr. Owens, the ear doctor who'd prescribed drops to cure a recent ear infection had ever thought much about my ears one way or another.

So for a few weeks after M. Luc's remark, I often looked at my ears in the mirror wondered why they were different from others except they didn't stick out as much as Clark Gable's open taxi-cab door ears.

Then one day Reg noticed me once again caressing one of M. Luc's "beautiful ears," and said, "Frances, I've noticed you rubbing your ears a lot lately, maybe you should make a date with Dr. Owens to see if that ear infection is back."

Meanwhile, in the car now driving back to Paris the only news I wanted to hear with my so-called beautiful ears was good news about retrieving my coat.

In Tourneys, Reg seemed in no hurry to get up from the Terminus restaurant's table after our lunch to make that important call to the George Blanc hotel.

"Reg, ask the waiter where the phones are."

Before he answered, he took another sip of his coffee. "Now be reasonable, Fran, it's too far to drive back. Look, forget that coat, when we get back to Paris, we'll go to Printemps department store and I'll buy you a new coat. You've had that one so long; it's bound to be almost worn out."

"Oh no, that Irish wool will last me a lifetime. Even though I've worn it on every trip we've ever taken, it still has years of wear left."

Reg sat there without saying anything for so long, I wasn't sure he'd heard me. Finally he said, "Since you've just told me that coat will never wear out, this is a good time to tell you that I've always hated it and couldn't wait for it to self-destruct…besides that puce color is a terrible color for you, makes you look as if you had jaundice."

To this day, I wonder if that coat is being worn in the village of Vonnas by a woman whose husband likes puce-colored cast-iron Irish wool, or is he too hoping in vain for the day it will wear out?

Miss French Flair

"Reg, take my share of the Concorde's caviar."

"…watching the slow Seine churned by bateaux-mouches *tour boats and dotted with seagulls, ducks and an occasional lost goose…"*

"…not in a hotel as usual but in our first rented apartment."

The surprise was that we were going to France in two months to stay for most of the summer, not in a hotel as usual but in our first rented apartment, courtesy of our friends Marie Therese Russell and her husband, Navy Captain Hawley Russell, aka Monk.

18 Quai de Bourbon

"Reg, take my share of the Concorde's caviar," I said as I placed a dish from my dinner tray onto his. "It's your favorite, but I'm a peasant, and I don't like slimy fish eggs."

At that moment Reg and I were strapped in our seats being shot across the Atlantic on a faster-than-the-speed-of-sound Concorde courtesy of Reg's employer, Lockheed.

Caviar is the only thing I disliked about the plane. Everything else was special, including no jet lag! Those long flights between San Francisco and Paris usually left me in a zombie-like state for days.

Sometimes I wonder if most of the world's decisions are made by business and political men and women suffering from impaired, jet-lagged mental states.

Reg was too busy scarfing down more caviar to pay attention to my observations, so I continued. "Probably this will be our last flight on this fantastic plane to Paris, so you'd better enjoy as much caviar as possible. Retiring next month cuts way back on caviar and French visits."

Reg still had a happy smile on his face when he said, "Sweetie, I know it's no hardship to part with fish eggs, so I'll save my gratitude for a homecoming surprise."

I reminded him that after thirty some-odd years of marriage, I had mixed feelings about surprises.

"Hope it's a new refrigerator. We've been away from California so often the past years, our kitchen needs new everything."

Since he seemed firm about no more discussion, I dropped the subject and enjoyed the rest of my Concorde dinner.

We'd been home in Menlo Park three days and I was still unpacking. I had the A.C./D.C. European converter kit in my hand when I remarked, "This goes in the storage closet, we won't need it for a long time, if ever."

Reg took it from my hand, saying, "No, no, I'll put it in my suitcase, we may need it for the surprise I promised."

"Surprise, oh yes, I remember, but we won't need this for any new appliances here."

How could I have been so clueless as to underestimate Reg's love of France and how it would have such an impact on his retirement years? I should have known that a man who was involved in putting astronauts on the moon would have no trouble getting us back to his now-beloved France."

The surprise was that we were going to France in two months, to stay for most of the summer, not in a hotel as usual but in our first rented apartment. Courtesy of our friends Marie Therese Russell and her husband, Navy Captain Hawley Russell, aka Monk. They had met with a young diplomat, Charles Stacy, who planned a long visit to his parents in San Francisco. Marie Therese asked if he would consider renting his apartment at 18 Quai de Bourbon on the Île St. Louis to a responsible retired couple from San Francisco.

For this gem, Mr. Stacy agreed on one condition. He did not have time to prepare for our stay: no cleaning up, no moving clothes, not even his maid Yvonne as she would be on vacation as well.

If this had been a film, I could see myself frozen in time, and the only words that registered were "our first rental."

"Rental, rental, that means housekeeping, doesn't it? No more room service, I'll be the room service?"

For sixteen years, from 1960 to 1976, Reg took me along to France to promote Lockheed's business interests between the United States and France. During those years, we stayed in our favorite hotel, the Prince de Gaulles. Suite 208 on the second floor became our home away from home. There I met two of the best friends I've ever had in this life, Marie Therese Russell and Michele le Menestrel (now Ullrich). Those two beautiful, intelligent, charming and kind French women epitomized the best example of the French people.

Michele and Marie Therese taught me many lessons, but not this one, because I never thought I'd need to know more about buying food than reading restaurant menus.

"Reg, I don't know how to keep house in France."

He claimed, "It's no different than what you do at home or in Atlanta."

I will never understand men.

He continued to sell me on how fortunate we would be in such an historic location, that the Parisians consider the small island their version of heaven.

On our first trip to France, I went there on a sightseeing tour. Our guide said it was the true heart of Paris. Paris began as a small island in the middle of the river that had not even been christened the Seine yet. In the fifth century under Clovis, one of the first Kings of France, one island became known as the Île de la Cité.

Across the Pont St. Louis is the petite Île St. Louis, a tiny pocket of the seventeenth century, surviving almost intact. It's a rabbit warren of narrow streets and along the quais are the famous old mansions.

"Dear, I remember a bit of the history, but that is the extent of my knowledge where we're going to live for the summer.

Never mind the history, I should have asked him to give me more details on M. Stacy's apartment.

Since Reg could sell bark off a tree, he continued to emphasize how lucky we were and assumed that if an Embassy diplomat lived there, it must be a very comfortable elegant apartment.

Time passed and we'd been settled in 18 Quai de Bourbon for a couple of days. The day we moved in the apartment after getting our luggage up the four flights of stairs with no elevator, I hoped the view was worth it. After inspecting the rooms, I immediately understood why the young bachelor M. Stacy had stipulated no cleaning up for the tenants. The place was a health hazard.

Therefore, my first priority was to get the place suitable for living. I would need quarts of the disinfectant cleaner Mr. Clean I used at home, and was sure they had a similar M. Propre here.

I prepared for my first marketing day as carefully as if I were to be presented at court. The concierge helped me make out a grocery list. At the door, she pointed to the left and said, "Madame Kearton, go down the rue Saint Louis en L'Île. Most of the markets are located at the other end of it."

With shopping list and a small French dictionary tucked in my basket, I followed her directions. At this time France did not have so many supermarkets with everything under one roof. The individual businesses and stores were the norm on the Île.

True to the concierge's words, the fish, meat, bakery, stationers, produce and post office were conveniently side by side along the Quai d'Anjou. The small town shops impart a village-like provincial calm.

The colorful produce market caught my eye first. For some time I stood on the pavement looking at the picture-perfect bins of vegetables, fruits and flowers, and wondered why French produce looks and tastes better than home.

Before I decided to go in, a man carrying a box of cerises came out from the back of the store. He gave me a pleasant smile and asked, "Madame, désirez-vous quelque chose?"

In my school French, I hesitantly said, "Oui, j'ai besoin de legumes." Then I ran out of French and continued in English, "But I don't know kilos, prices or how much to buy or some of the names unless I look them up in this. " And I pulled out my little dictionary.

He began to laugh. "Oh Madame, we have many English customers. I can help you with anything you need."

Suddenly a wave of homesickness came over me. He was standing by the artichoke bin and for some reason the sight of the artichokes reminded me of home. Castroville is the artichoke capital of California. The moving in and the prospect of all I had to do to clean up the apartment brought on my childhood stammer. I flapped my hands up and down and before I made a total fool of myself I said, "Never mind. Pardonnez moi" and turned to leave.

The man seemed to sense my distress. He beckoned to the billowy woman with a rosy-cheeked pretty face who was sitting at the cash register. They introduced themselves as Monsieur and Madame Barbier, owners of the freshest and best produce market in Paris. They were both so cheerful and friendly, I began to relax. I confided to them why I seemed so upset. After sixteen years of living in hotels on our Paris visits, I now had to learn how to keep house at the 18 Quai de Bourbon apartment we had leased for the summer. Since they had been here on the Île for many years and knew all the other shopkeepers, they promised to give me good advice.

The next day when I returned, M. Barbier greeted me like his pupil. "Ah Ah Madame, une leçon pour les légumes et les fruits. Aujourd'hui nous avons les petits pois en saison et aussi des pêches."

Along with the names, the day I bought some asparagus, Madame teasingly winked at me and said "Are you sure you want them? In the 17th century upper class women never ate asparagus because they thought it was bad for reproductions". I raised my eyebrows and said, "Heaven forbid, I had better eat a lot of it them. We have enough children already."

Another day, I overbought and didn't have enough francs to cover my bill. When I began to return the cantaloupes, Madame put them back in my basket and said, "Non, non, demain, demain. Pas de problème." I had a mental picture of a clerk at my Safeway supermarket at home saying, "Never mind, pay the rest tomorrow."

The Barbiers gave me more confidence in my new role of American in Paris living on the Île that Parisians call Heaven.

After a few weeks, I felt as if I'd lived on the Île forever. I'd even discovered a beauty salon and was considered a regular client since the apartment's plumbing did not lend itself to comfortable shampooing. One must sit in tub to use a handheld shower attachment. The trickle of water from the apparatus was so spasmodic, the soap lather had dried into a hardened helmet before I could rinse it off.

The problem was solved on one of my exploratory walks in the Île's narrow, mysterious streets lined with the past written in stone, made easy to read on the marble historical plaques on half of the mossy landmark townhouses designed in the 1600s.

I stopped to remove a pebble from my shoe in front of an unassuming coiffeuse shop wedged against the medieval Catholique Saint Louis en Île church opposite "L'Orangerie," a favorite restaurant we'd visited with Michele and her mother Mila. A perfect location for a beauty salon - your hair could be coiffed Saturday before church on Sunday.

When I glimpsed several women sitting under hair dryers instead of having the new blow-dried unisex fashion, I knew my hair had found its rightful place.

The following day I returned in late afternoon to make an appointment, but I missed the magic hour of 5:30pm. The various times of opening and closing of the shops is a Wheel of Fortune gamble.

18 Quai de Bourbon

While I was reading the clock placard on the door, an attractive middle-aged woman (or "dame d'un certain age," a gentler French description of a woman no longer in the first blush of youth), came to the door. She had fire engine red hair arranged in the latest beehive bouffant style. I assumed she was the Madame of the Madame Solange's Maison de Beauté. She smiled and with an apologetic shrug pointed to the Ferme sign.

I smiled back and mouthed, "demain?" We began a pantomime performance equaling the famous French mime, Marcelle Marceau.

Pointing to my hair, I acted out a shampoo, and scissors for un appointement demain, Mercredi. Madame checked her appointment book after which we mutually understood I was to be there tomorrow at 2 p. m. for a shampoo, cut and set.

The next day I arrived on time and was pleased to know I was to be Madame Solange's client. At the time I had thick blonde hair. Past experience had taught me it brings out hair dressers' urge to experiment a la fashion magazines.

By pulling up a handful of hair to demonstrate to Madame I wished ends to be "en haut," she looked puzzled. I wanted it UP instead of Under. She clapped her hands and said, "Ah Madame, je comprends. Vous voulez extérieur."

French is a maddening language for the English because so many words including those we have borrowed come so close to English. Yet, my school Latin classes were no help. The words don't mean the same. I thought "haut" meant "up," which it does, and "extérieur" meant "outside" of a building.

Never mind, my hair was looking better under Madame Solange's care whether it was styled exterior or interior or sous. Just like home, artistic hair dressers live in a world of their own.

I walked home after the Wednesday session rather satisfied with myself. Maybe Reg would notice my new image, the result of overcoming another successful challenge in a foreign country.

When I returned to 18 Quai de Bourbon, my smug self-congratulatory feeling didn't last long. Reg was gazing intently out of the large front window at the ever-changing river traffic. The light was fading then, but he could still see the bank's walkway, where the young lovers, Gene Kelly and Leslie Caron danced in the classic "American in Paris" film.

I asked, "How do you like my new French hair style done by Madame Solange?"

He turned, gave me a brief glance, and said "Fran, very nice, do it the same for our party."

Long ago, I learned that Reg has a very very quick mind. He once told me when he decides something in his own mind he goes on to other plans. And forgets he has failed to communicate his decisions. Such as to wife, Fran wondering what he meant by "our party".

I didn't say anything and waited for what was coming next. And had the feeling it was to be another challenge far more complicated than Madame Solange's hair styling.

"Fran, I have an idea. We've always had to entertain our French friends in hotels and restaurants. Now for awhile we have this unique place. It's a perfect time and place for a real party."

Picking up an open book from the coffee table, he continued, "I've been reading about the Île. Did you know it's called the Artistic Island of Paris? As an artist, you should feel at home here."

Not wishing for Reg to digress on Island history and away from the main subject, I asked, "What else do you have in mind by 'party'? We've already entertained most of our closest friends here for cocktails then out for dinner."

He claimed we had many more friends, former business associates, people from the Paris embassy and acquaintances that haven't been here. With the help of Michele and Marie Therese, he'd take responsibility for guest list and invitations.

He kept pacing around the big room and finally stopped to say, "If the party is from 5-8 with wine, cocktails and a buffet of substantial hors d'oeuvres, we could have at least forty people and probably more in this room. You give great parties at home so you can do the same here."

Every now and then, I have a fleeting moment when I remember the after-the-fact advice an astrologer sent me when I married Reg in 1954. She cautioned about a Tauran marrying an Aquarian, even if the Aquarian's mother was a Taurus with the same April 24th birth date. At times we are on different outer space stations.

Reg broadened my horizons in so many ways but sometimes he pushed those horizons too far off the horizon for comfort. As usual we compromised: okay for the party, but three weeks instead of two. Maybe M and Mme Barbier at the produce place will help me.

I'd made some inroads on M. Stacy's bachelor college dormitory style living. But my days of taking time out from one of my favorite occupations, watching the slow Seine churned by bateaux-mouches tour boats and dotted with seagulls, ducks and an occasional lost goose had to be put aside. A party with many guests for the first time hastens a hostess's desire to show the best company face.

The place obviously needed more of a woman's touch than he gets from his maid Yvonne. Considering the many female phone calls and the disappointed sighs when I'd say, "M. Stacy n'est pas ici. Il est à San Francisco," he didn't lack for a woman's touch in *some* ways.

Yet, I wondered if any of those young-sounding women could give him some heavy duty help in keeping the place reasonably habitable. Perhaps that was not a priority.

A photo in the apartment of him on skis indicated an unmarried blonde handsome young man in the admirable occupation of "diplomat" who lived in one of the most sought after addresses in Paris. He has an oversized bed in the front room, plus an unusual collection of African masks, spears and carvings from his recent assignment in Kenya. The living room also had a well stocked bar and that incredible view.

At night with candles lit and some champagne, who cares if bedrooms, kitchen and bathroom should be reported to the local health inspector? In fact, in my salad days, I probably would have climbed those four flights with him to see the spectacular view of Notre Dame across the Seine on the Île de la Cité. Not many young bachelors have that to offer as an enticement for that last nightcap.

Yet until a few days before the party, all the female voices had no faces. I'd continued my efforts to make the apartment a bit less Bohemian and scrape some of the decades of dirt from the surfaces. One would think I was a meticulous housekeeper at home. Far from it, but preparing for guests brings out what latent talent I had.

Therefore, the day before the party, I decided the black and white tiles at the entrance needed attention. The white tiles were more grey than white.

Dressed in my cleaning outfit of rubber gloves, blue jeans, one of Reg's old shirts and hair tucked in a Monoprix copy of a Hermes scarf, I was on my knees vigorously attacking the tiles with a scrub brush and bucket of Mr. Clean soapy water when the doorbell rang.

I said "Entrez."

The door opened. I looked up from my kneeling position and there stood a clone of Viennese native American MGM movie star who had just been voted the most beautiful woman in the world, Hedy LaMarr.

This unexpected gorgeous creature dressed in a beige Chanel suit stood there holding a bulging laundry bag. She had as surprised a look on her exquisite face as I did on my no-make-up not-ready-for-the-public one.

Still holding the bag, she looked down on me and said, "Oh, I thought you were Yvonne. I know Charles is away but she does my laundry when she does his. You must be Yvonne's substitute."

Scrub brush in hand, I hastily removed the ersatz Hermes scarf from my head and struggled up off my knees. I said in an almost apologetic voice, "no, I'm not Yvonne but I think she could do a better job than Françoise, that's me."

Before I had a chance to clear up Miss Gorgeous' confusion and introduce myself as Charles' temporary tenant, she impatiently dumped the heavy laundry bag on my newly scrubbed tiles. With a dismissive wave of her elegantly manicured hand, her last words as she began her descent down the stairs were, "Never mind, I'll pay you the same if you do the job as well as Yvonne."

When she was halfway down the stairs, she turned around and shouted, "Forgot to tell you, no starch in the shirts".

The last order was the proverbial straw. Wondering where to store a large bag of dirty clothes here in this already overcrowded apartment gave me an irresistible impulse to push Miss Gorgeous with her laundry bag down the four flights of stairs.

The past few weeks of hard unaccustomed work involved in making the apartment livable plus the strain of party preparations had left me feeling like Cinderella in the ashes.

At least I had the good sense to wait until she had reached the bottom of the stairs. Dragging the bag out and balancing it on the banister rail, I gave it a hard push. She saw it flying down the stairs and jumped aside just as the bag landed by the front door.

She let out some language which I don't think proper for a refined young lady in either French or English. Although I imagine stupide, chienne (bitch) and idiot are understandable in both languages.

I retaliated by saying, "You didn't stay long enough for me to introduce myself as one of M. Stacy's summer tenants, and your laundry is not in the contract."

Then I did something so childish, or maybe plain old jealousy or nostalgia that I am ashamed to tell on myself. I yelled down, "I may look like Yvonne's replacement today, but once I was a model for the John Robert Powers agency in New York. Powers boasted that on his roster he had the hundred most beautiful girls in the United States. So there."

Now, really, what was I thinking? Well, I wasn't going to invite her to our party anyway.

Miss Gorgeous missed a good party. If she'd been polite I might have invited her just to give the men a treat. On the other hand, most of the men's wives could hold their own. French women can do more with a scarf that most of us can with a closet filled with designer clothes. It must be something in their DNA.

That fleeting thought was dismissed immediately. I had enough on my plate without coping with one of M. Stacy's harem. Even working in a well-equipped familiar kitchen, I suffer from pre-party apprehension. Here in a kitchen barely sufficient in which to boil an egg plus guests speaking another language, one I spoke so poorly, the apprehension settled into eagle size butterflies in my midsection.

Then I remembered the Red Queen's instructions to Alice in Alice in the Looking Glass, when she said, "Speak in French when you can't think of the English for a thing...turn out your toes when you walk, and remember who you are."

If I changed the Queen's speech in English when I can't think of the French, and remembered who I was, a native of Georgia, one of the original thirteen states of the United States of America, I'd follow Reg's advice to plan the same as if I were at home.

With the menu settled, it was fun to prepare the buffet: potato salad, deviled eggs, fried chicken drumsticks (easy to handle), cheese biscuits, watermelon pickles if possible, and homemade chocolate brownies plus ice cream. The Berthillon Glacier of the famed ice cream makers was around the corner on 31 rue Saint Louis en l'Île.

When Reg and I explained to the manager that we were Californians giving our first party on the Île, he was more than helpful. He offered to send ice cream packed in ice at the proper time. Then my newfound friends, the produce market Barbiers suggested Madame prepare platters of 'crudities' such as radishes, spring onions, celery, tomatoes, and carrots. This was before such became standard cocktail fare in the States.

When one of the women guests asked for my potato salad recipe, I was pleased the party was going so well and Reg was enjoying the successful host role. He'd discovered in the Île's artistic history our address at 18 Quai de Bourbon was surrounded by former illustrious writers and artists. Reg bragged his wife Fran was also an artist so she felt at home here.

Sometimes Reg gets carried away and I wish he had skipped that reference. My paintings were a long long way from such formidable ghosts of the past. Those neighbors lived too many centuries ago to either give me painting lessons or lend me a cup of sugar.

Before anyone showed interest in my paintings of flowers, trees and landscapes, I welcomed a change of subject until I realized the change was for the worse.

Sharing his newfound knowledge on our long deceased neighbors, Reg pointed out that next door 19 Quai de Bourbon had been the ground floor studio of sculptor Camille Claudel, Rodin's protégé and lover. After his statement, Christian LeBrun from the American Embassy challenged Reg. Christian insisted Claudel's studio was on the other side, number 15.

If Reg was going to disagree with the French on newly acquired French history, I was relieved he chose an American to do it with. The two men agreed to settle the debate by going down the stairs on to the Quai. A gentle breeze was blowing in from Le Havre, and at dusk it was still light enough to read the marble historical plaques on numbers 19 and 15.

That seems a better way to end the matter amicably than the former days of pistols or swords at dawn in the Bois de Boulogne until I realized we were losing our party.

Reg and Christian were like the Pied Piper because half the guests were following them down the stairs to read the plaques to judge for themselves.

Looking down from the picture window, I saw our guests walking up and down the Quai going from house to house, reading the plaques. It was like watching actors in a silent movie. The guests were waving their arms, pointing to different plaques and shaking their heads. To me, it looked more like pistols at dawn in the Bois than a gentlemanly settlement on ancient history.

Turning away from the scene I sat down on M. Stacy's acre-size bed and burst into tears.

Dear friends Michele and Marie Therese stayed and joined me on the bed. Michele hugged me and explained, "Ma chérie, if you had planned it, you couldn't have dreamed up better entertainment. It rivals anything the Embassy could provide. You aren't looking at quarreling. The French, in particular French men, love nothing better than to argue about history and politics."

Marie Therese chimed in. "Once I took visitors from Lyon to the Arts et Traditions Populaires and they spent half an hour counting and recounting the buttons on the fabric lining in a carriage. Some claimed the carriage had too many buttons on it for the decade listed on the descriptions."

True to her advice, all the guests returned, and felt superior to the latecomers in retelling what they had missed. It must have been a good party because even running out of food, it lasted until nearly midnight. When I went to bed with a smile on my face, a few diehards were still arguing that the 1659 townhouse on the Quai de Bourbon goes by the name "House of the Centaur" for some reason or another. I fell asleep before I learned the answer to that nonlife-threatening question. I was just pleased that Madame St. Denis asked for my potato salad recipe.

Sometimes I hear fellow Americans repeat the timeworn phrase, "France is a beautiful country, if only it wasn't filled with Frenchmen". Well, if Frenchmen took a week's tour of the States, they might feel the same. If visitors see only the usual tourist attractions, they miss the real France. Even if we only have one example to rebut that misconception, I will remember the kindness shown to us by the residents the summer we spent on the magic Île Saint Louis.

To add to the Île example, I recall so much help we have received from considerate and warmhearted French strangers on our travels.

Once we drove from Paris to Strasbourg for a music festival. Arriving in a sudden cloudburst, the rain was so heavy it was difficult to see the street signs and we were unable to find our hotel. Reg pulled off in front of a restaurant and said, "Dash in there and ask directions."

Before I could get out of the car, a sweet-faced elderly woman came out of the restaurant and stood under the awning. I rolled down my window and asked her if she knew the way to the Hotel Au Cerf d'Or. She gave a negative head shake, but raising her hand said, "Un moment, attendez. Je le trouve" and disappeared into the restaurant.

She returned. Leaning over into the car window, she handed me explicit directions to the hotel written on a paper napkin.

She laughed. "Here, take this quick before the rain gets it as wet as I am."

Strasbourg's music festivals are known worldwide, but my most vivid memory of the city is the sight of this woman, standing in the rain, giving two lost travelers a damp napkin with hotel directions written on it.

Before we left 18 Quai de Bourbon for home, we took a night time scenic tour of Paris at the bewitching midnight hour when the traffic was light. I caught my breath when we drove over the Pont Alexandre III, the prettiest bridge in Paris. It was built between 1896 and 1900 to commemorate the French Russian alliance, and the Universal Exhibition. I could have spent hours on that bridge, with its Art Nouveau decoration of gilt and bronze lamps, cupids and cherubs, nymphs and winged horses at either end. That is the trouble with Paris. It would take more than one lifetime to see and learn its wonders.

Reg drove slowly so we could enjoy the magnificent views of the lights on the Grand Palais, the Champs-Elysees and the Invalides.

When I was sixteen years old, an astrologer predicted I would spend a great deal of time in Paris, and the City would capture my heart.

Perhaps there is no love without pain and some of my suffering in life has been in Paris. In the long run, the love far outweighs the pain. At least I was suffering in the most beautiful city in the world.

The Colonel's Wife

All of Paris lay at our feet.

"Oh, Nita, isn't it beautiful, wonderful, gorgeous?"

I spread my arms wide and twirled around twice, much to the amusement of two other tourists at the far end of the Tour Eiffel platform.

"I've dreamed of coming here all my life." I pinched myself. "Yep, I'm here…Paris in the spring, chestnut trees blooming and all."

Guidebook in hand, I pointed and said "See that beautiful white dome? That's the Sacre Coeur." Nita, Mrs. Lionel Putt, wife of a retired colonel now employed by the same aircraft company in California as my husband Reg, and I were accompanying the men on a business trip.

In 1957 I'd been a corporate wife for only a short while, so when Reg told me that he was being sent to Paris for almost a month, my face fell. "Well, c'est la cotton pickin' vie…so far you've taken me along to the garden spots of the world." I began to tick them off on my fingers. "Huntsville, Alabama; White Sands, New Mexico; and Kansas City, Missouri…red clay, sand dunes and stockyards."

I was on the verge of tears. "And now, you're going to Paris without me."

"Fran, you didn't let me finish. The boss man thinks Colonel Putt and I'll stay out of trouble better in Gay Paree if our wives come along…besides, there's lots of entertaining involved." Throwing my arms around him, I shouted "whoopee! And Nita with me is icing on the cake…it'll be fun to have someone sightsee with me. I met Nita at the last big company party. She seems pleasant."

So here we were, two American wives on the Tour Eiffel platform, fulfilling the dream of a lifetime—or mine, at any rate.

My enthusiasm for our birds-eye view of Paris was in contrast to Nita's lack of same. She glanced briefly in the direction of the world renowned church and sniffed, "It doesn't look very big. Our Methodist church in Charles City, Iowa is a lot bigger than that dinky thing. I remember, when we added a wing, Reverend Cosgrove said I was the best fundraiser he'd ever had. 'Course, that was before I married the Colonel." She reached over, pulled my shirt collar out from under my sweater and gave it a pat. "There, that's better…say, did I ever tell you how I met the Colonel?"

No, I thought, you haven't told me how you met the Colonel, but that's about the only thing you haven't told me. Or maybe that nugget of information was lost among tales of relatives, movie plots, dreams you've had and your authoritative knowledge on cooking, jewelry, what to order in a restaurant, which shops have the best bargains in gloves and earrings, and other subjects too numerous to list.

One particular case filled with bejeweled timepieces prompted Nita to say "Dali, I know, he's the one who paints all those weirdo limp watches?"

No limp watches in this photo of Fran with her paintings, shown at Le Salon des Nations à Paris, 1983.

Nita and I'd been together constantly since leaving the San Francisco airport a week ago. To say that I was weary of her endless monologues would be an understatement—like the Mississippi River, they kept rolling along and nothing could divert them. I tried, though.

"Look over there, the Arc de Triomphe."

Before she leaned towards the railing for a better view, she tightened the screws on her earrings, two miniature champagne glasses. "I'd hate to lose these, don't you love them…so Paris, don't you think?" My unfamiliarity with French laws on the subject of justifiable homicide made me quickly dismiss the urge to give her a push. Inasmuch as Nita was several inches taller than my five foot six and was sturdy as all get out with muscles developed from Iowa fundraising, I doubted that I could toss her over. Besides, the protective barrier made the whole idea an impossibility. Still, it was an attractive thought.

How could my romantic dream of being in the City of Light with a man I loved have turned into a nightmare by such an incompatible traveling companion? Nita and I were handcuffed for the duration! I wondered if she secretly felt the same way about me. No, it wasn't possible, since nothing was a secret with Nita.

The discovery that our goals on this trip were as far apart as the Poles surfaced immediately. My desire to cram in as many museums, galleries, historical places and old bookstores was diametrically opposed to Nita's desire to cover an equal number of small shops and large department stores.

The compromise we'd agreed upon wasn't working out, because we spent a lot more time at the Bon Marché than we did at the Louvre. Each time I suggested splitting up, I heard the same

72

refrain, "Just a minute more, Fran, I've got to find a baby present for my niece, and as long as we're here, let's look at earrings."
At first, husband Reg thought my predicament funny. When he realized that her non-stop chatter during our nightly entertaining of potential French business associates interfered with his aims, he became more sympathetic. After one long, expensive and ultimately frustrating evening in which he'd hoped to get some important points across to our guests in a subtle manner, he said, "I don't know how she does it."

Half asleep, I muttered "Who does what?"

"Nita—every time I manage to steer the conversation on to space exploration, she slogs it out 'til she gets it back to something she wants to talk about. I wish I could harness her gift."

"Why don't you have Lionel give her a hint, or shove, or whatever it takes?"

"She's got Lionel so hogtied he wouldn't dare."

A week later while we were dressing for dinner, Reg said "Tonight it's General Pierre Gallois. He's NATO. Madame'll be with him, you and Nita…plus two extra men from the Paris office, Jean Luis and Robbie...reservations at Laurent's." My mind wasn't on the guest list. I was giving myself a critical last minute once-over in the bathroom door's mirror. The black silk pleated dress had looked so sophisticated in the small shop on Main Street in Los Altos, California. Now I wasn't sure if it was up to Laurent. I'd read that the restaurant on Avenue Gabriel near the American Embassy was one of the most beautiful in Paris. It was a romantic spot with an outside terrace, tables set in tiers, and an orchestra. In my head, I was dancing there with Reg when he brought me back to the task at hand.

"This is supposed to be a social evening, but Pete Gallois has been as elusive as smoke. It's my last chance to pin him down. Put Nita in between the two extra fellows. Or, better yet, out in the Bois de Boulogne."

"Nope, protocol says Nita and me on either side of the General, you and Lionel ditto for Madame. You'll have to talk across the table."

"Fat chance, I need his ears along. Nita'll be telling him about her Uncle Charley." Reg had a second thought. "Oh God, even worse, she'll tell him how to run NATO! See what you can do."

I had no idea how I could pull off that tall order, but the Laurent's dance orchestra came to my rescue. When the music began, I asked Reg to dance with me. He couldn't gracefully refuse, but he grumbled all the way out to the floor.

"This is not helping me talk to Pete."

"Oh, yes it is, look, it worked…Pete's dancing with Madame, and Lionel has Nita in tow".

Reg box-stepped me around to the other side of the room before continuing his complaints. "Well, what the hell are we supposed to do on the dance floor, send up smoke signals? Nita has talked poor Pete into a coma, and Madame has that same look on her face you get when you can't stand another minute of corporate talk."

After Reg heard my game plan, he calmed down and said, "It's worth a try." We left the floor before the orchestra finished the set in order to give the two bachelors their assignments.

When Madame and Nita returned to the table with their husbands, the Frenchmen were to invite the two women to dance. Between them, they were to keep the women on the dance floor for the rest of the evening.

Both women bloomed with the attention. Madame Gallois made no more let's go home signals, and Reg, Lionel and the General were left in deep conversation. I sat there at the table in semi-isolation. While I tapped my feet in time to the music and fingered the pleats on my black silk skirt, I did my best not to notice that the two Frenchmen were superb dancers.

Once, Nita waltzed by and leaned over my shoulder to whisper, "Fran, I've suggested to Robbie that he dance with you, but he says he's never had a better partner...doesn't want to miss a minute."

"Thanks Nita, I'm tired anyway. Some of us got it and some ain't...tonight, you've got it." She waltzed on, a happy smile on her face, the belle of Paree.

Back at the hotel, Reg was pleased with the evening's outcome. "But sweetie, I'm sorry you had such a thin time of it".

"No, I didn't really. I sort of enjoyed being a junior Mata Hari." I giggled. "It was almost worth it to see Nita so busy working her feet, she forgot to work her mouth!"

An irritating companion couldn't spoil my enjoyment of Paris, and before I knew it, we had only a week left. My plans for those last precious days were shot to pieces when Reg announced that he and Lionel had to make an unplanned trip to Italy.

"Oh, Reg, can't I go with you? Now I'll have a steady diet of Nita morning, noon AND night." Reg commiserated but there was nothing to be done about it.

The first evening after the men left, I wanted to have soup in the room until Nita convinced me otherwise.

"We're here several days without the fellows. No point in staying holed up like timid mice at night. Right now, we're going downstairs to the Espadon Restaurant. Tomorrow we'll go someplace else." This was one time I appreciated her bossiness.

While we were riding the elevator down, it stopped on the floor below us and another couple entered. When I recognized them, I nudged Nita and rolled my eyes but she ignored me. When we reached the lobby, the man with his famous mustache and flowing cape disappeared out the revolving doors. I turned to Nita and said, "Did you see them, that was Salvador Dali and his wife Gayla?"

"No, I was trying to get a better look at the woman's ears in front of me. She had on the most adorable fruit basket earrings, didn't you see them?"

"Nita, since I don't wear earrings, I don't give them much thought."

While walking along the long corridor towards the restaurant, we stopped from time to time to look at the glittering showcases featuring the expensive wares from the rue Saint-Honoré shops. One particular case filled with bejeweled timepieces prompted Nita to say "Dali, I know, he's the one who paints all those weirdo limp watches?"

After we were seated in the restaurant, Nita continued "Paintings aren't my specialty; my specialty is antique sick cups. When we get home, I'll show you my collection, over a hundred now."

"Hiccups, how can you collect hiccups?"

"Silly girl, I said sick cups. They're Aladdin's lamp-shaped holders with a spout. Before straws, they were used to feed liquids to invalids."

"How'd you begin to collect something so esoteric? You didn't just wake up one morning and think, Gee today I start collecting sick cups."

We were interrupted by the waiter asking for our order but all that talk of sick cups was making me queasy. I wasn't hungry and the room began to swim around me. I felt so dizzy that my one instinct was to leave the table and head for the terrace and fresh air.

"Nita, I don't feel so…" And that's the last I remembered until I woke up in our hotel room with Nita and a strange man hovering over me. The only conversation I heard before lapsing into unconsciousness again came from Nita. "Yes, Dr. Brunet, I'll stay with her tonight…okay, she'll get one every four hours."

Later I learned that I'd fallen flat on my face beside the table. The horrified maitre d' had rushed over but Nita indignantly corrected his initial assumption that I'd had too much wine. She told me that she'd said the first thing that came to mind.

"Madame's had a heart attack…call a doctor toot sweet."

My illness wasn't fatal; it just felt that way—a particularly virulent case of la grippe. During the next few days, in addition to being sick, I was so guilt ridden that I thought I'd never crawl out of that soft swamp bog which passed for a mattress in France.

How could I have imagined that Nita's Clydesdale horse face was homely? I now realized how full of character and kindness it was. And how could I have thought this woman tiresome and annoying?

Three days and nights, Nita stayed with me. She fed me custards and broths, order the waiters around, plumped my pillows—and talked. I grew to love her long monotonous stories about Aunt Wiley and her herb bed, the bank president cousin, Gene Posslethwaite, and other denizens of Charles City.

When the men returned to Paris, Reg couldn't believe I'd been ill because I'd recovered so well.

"If I'm still alive, I give Nita full credit. She was a Godsend, and a crackerjack nurse. I'm ashamed it took a 103 degree fever for me to appreciate her."

At the end of the return trip to San Francisco, we parted ways with the Putts at the top of an airport escalator. After Nita had given me a goodbye hug, she unclasped the small onyx owl pin which perched on the right shoulder of my suit, pinned it over on the left, and said "Much better. Listen, when our pictures come back, I'll call you. We'll get together at our house 'cause remember, I promised to show you my collection of antique sick cups."

When the escalator had taken them halfway down, Nita turned back for one last wave and yelled, "And I never did tell you how I met the Colonel."

On the way home in our car, Reg said "That's good, I'm glad you and Nita got along. We'll probably have to travel with them again."

"If we do, leave me home."

Reg gave me a puzzled look. "But I thought you said...." He stopped in mid-sentence, shook his head and gave man's oft-repeated utterance since the time of Adam and Eve,

"I'll never, ever understand women."

The Colonel's Wife

I spread my arms wide and twirled around twice, much to the amusement of two other tourists at the far end of the Tour Eiffel platform.

Eiffel Tower ⑭

★ **Viewing Gallery**
On a clear day it is possible to see for 72 km (45 miles), including a distant view of Chartres Cathedral.

Eiffel Tower
een from the
'rocadéro

BUILT FOR the Universal Exhibition of 1889, and to commemorate the centennial of the Revolution, the 320-m (1,051-ft) Eiffel Tower (Tour Eiffel) was meant to be a temporary addition to Paris's skyline. Designed by Gustave Eiffel, it was fiercely decried by 19th-century aesthetes. It stood as the world's tallest building until 1931, when New York's Empire State Building was completed.

"My San Francisco dentist warned me about putting anything gummy on it for awhile..."

The Gold Crown

Nita Putt and I were on our first visit to Paris thanks to our husbands' employer, Lockheed Aircraft Corporation—our husbands for business, and us for pleasure. Since our arrival, we'd stayed in a constant high fever of excitement.

A priority in our blitzkrieg of sightseeing was the Tour Eiffel. With Michelin guides in hand, we were now on our fifth lap around its viewing platform.

As we stood waiting for a German couple to relinquish a stationary telescope, Nita held out a paper sack and said "Here, Fran, have a French caramel. I bought these at the Godiva candy store near the Ritz."

"Might as well," I whispered. "These people are taking so long to zero in on the Notre Dame, I think they are using a Rome guidebook instead of Paris."

As I popped one of the caramels into my mouth, I said, "I'll see if French caramels are different from California caramels."

After a couple of chews, I spit it back in its paper wrapper, walked a few steps and tossed it in a trash can. Nita gave me a puzzled look. "What's the matter, Fran, French caramels can't be that bad, not at French prices anyway."

I laughed "No, it was delicious, what little I tasted, but I remembered my new gold back molar crown. My San Francisco dentist warned me about putting anything gummy on it for awhile."

Nita said, "Hah, you're lucky to have some teeth left for a caramel to stick to."

"Hum, the basics are still my own, but most of them have been fortified with enough gold to make me the walking wealthy."

By that time, the German couple was having a dispute on whether to put any more francs in the telescope slot. Apparently the most frugal of the pair, the woman won, so they drifted off.

After Nita and I had thoroughly exhausted the pigeon-eye views of the City of Light from the telescope, we left the platform for the Tour Eiffel's back-to-earth funicular. Midway down, I felt the chilly Paris wind was giving me a new sensation in pain each time I opened my mouth. Upon further exploration, my tongue discovered the reason, a hole which felt like the Grand Canyon where my new crown had been. At the end of the return ride, I grabbed Nita's hand and raced over to the funicular's UP waiting line. To my bewildered friend, I wailed, "Nita, we have to go back up to look for my crown. "

Back on the platform, I walked over to our last stop, the telescope, and stood beside the nearby trash can.

I explained "My mother taught me not to litter so I threw my caramel in here. The crown must have stuck in it, but how do we find it?"

At that moment, one of the platform's security guards walked by. I won't go into the lengthy description on what it took for us to convince the puzzled guard that my crown was not where it belonged but stuck in a caramel somewhere in that particular trash bin. I would have been hard put to explain that in any language.

At last, with pantomiming and showing of empty space in my mouth, accompanied by our fractured French, he understood the problem. With Gallic gallantry, he overturned the bin and together we rummaged through the trash. Sure enough, the guard found that precious crown stuck in the caramel. He was so pleased to have struck California gold and promoted Franco-American relationships, he escorted us back to the funicular and waved goodbye with many good luck wishes.

The next problem was how to get the gold crown back where it belonged.

Nita said "Fran, ask the Ritz concierge to make a dental appointment for you. That's what he's there for—to help the hotel guests."

"You could have fooled me." I hadn't had the nerve to ask him anything else since I handed him a 500 franc note for taxi change. Maybe I didn't pronounce "Taxi" with the proper accent because his hand came out like the mysterious one in a black box sold in joke shops. He grabbed the note and said "Merci pour le pourboire." He was thanking me for the tip. I had wanted it changed for the taxi, but I didn't have the courage to correct him.

"Fran, he speaks beautiful English, so he'll call a dentist for you."

When we returned to the Ritz, Nita left me at the entrance for her Elizabeth Arden Hair appointment next door. Without her support and before tackling the haughty concierge, I reminded myself that though we weren't royalty or jet set members, we were paying the same price for our rooms as their more renowned guests.

After reaching his lofty perch near the entrance, all thoughts of attempting to act as if I were a sophisticated frequent guest vanished. I was in too much pain to practice my schoolgirl French. Instead I resorted to pantomime by opening my mouth, then holding out the missing caramel-impaled gold crown for his inspection.

At the sight of my obvious dilemma, a Dr. Jekyll and Mr. Hyde transformation came over the Concierge. His imperious, intimidating persona turned into one of immediate concern. He said in beautiful Oxford English, "Wait here, Madame Kearton, while I call a dentist."

As he was talking to the dentist's receptionist on the phone, I wondered why he kept shaking his head back and forth and hoped that didn't indicate no appointment available. Then I overheard him say in an authoritative tone of voice, "Non, non, pas demain, maintenant." I understood enough French to know that he was insisting that this emergency couldn't wait until tomorrow.

He must have convinced the receptionist because he hung up and said, "Can you leave immediately? The dentist's office is near and it's faster to walk than taxi. I'll go with you a short way until we reach boulevard Malesherbes ."

Since the light drizzle which had begun on our taxi ride from the Tour Eiffel had developed into a steady downpour, he produced an oversized umbrella from behind his desk and off we went.

During our walk, he assured me that he could recommend Dr. Ravier from personal experience. Only last month the dentist had successfully treated his abscessed tooth. When I said, "Oh, I can sympathize. In my youth I suffered from two abscessed teeth," he responded, "Oh, Madame Kearton, at least you know. Unless one has experienced such pain firsthand, even your family doesn't understand."

By the time he'd finished with his tooth story we'd reached boulevard Malesherbes. After thrusting his written directions in my hand along with the umbrella, he turned and began running bareheaded in the rain back to the hotel.

After he'd left me, I felt as if I'd parted with an old friend—nothing like mutual misery memories to bond even the most disparate of people.

As I began walking down the boulevard Malesherbes , I'd forgotten to ask the Concierge if I was on the same side of the wide boulevard as Dr. Ravier's office. In order to refresh my memory on the correct number, I clutched the large Ritz umbrella with one hand, while holding the Concierge's written address paper out from under its protection, to better to read it.

Major mistake. It seemed to me it was always raining during any crisis of mine. The heavy rain washed over the paper smearing the address. Therefore, I couldn't decide if Dr. Ravier's address was 103 or 108.

103 proved to be on the wrong side of the boulevard so by the time I'd found the dentist's office, my windblown rain-soaked state of appearance only aggravated my inner terror.

When I walked into the waiting room and told the nurse receptionist I had an appointment with Dr. Ravier, she looked at me in disbelief and said, "Non, non, impossible. His next appointment was made by the Ritz Hotel's concierge for a guest from the hotel."

I pointed to myself and said "Moi."

With some reluctance, the nurse indicated a chair in the waiting room and said the Doctor would see me presently. After I settled myself, I didn't wonder at her seeming reluctance to have me sit on one of their Louis Quatorze chairs in my damp clothing. The entire room must have been furnished from the Louvre Museum's antique furniture wing.

And when I was ushered into Dr. Ravier's office, the same could be said of it. The only piece of furniture which indicated he was a dentist was the dental chair. Nothing else resembled the no-nonsense sterile, efficient-looking office of my San Francisco dentist.

By then, the events of the day had left me so demoralized, I was virtually speechless, and reduced to sign language. Every memory of difficult dental visits from age six on resurfaced. A session with a familiar dentist at home is not first on the list of fun things to do, but a visit to an unknown one in a foreign country is at the bottom. And this unknown's physical appearance was far from reassuring. To me, Dr. Ravier resembled Bela Lugosi in his role of Count Dracula.

After a perfunctory bonjour greeting, the doctor asked, "Parlez-vous Français?"

I gave a negative shake of my head and repeated the same pantomime I'd used on the concierge.

But Dr. Ravier was determined to find a more verbal method of communication. I assumed that my Nordic appearance was what prompted him to try German, which I could recognize yet not understand. He then switched to a Scandinavian sounding one.

Finally I came out of my self-induced "fear of dentists" state and said that I was from California, which last I'd heard was in the United States.

He claimed that his English was not "parfait," but it was fluent enough for me to understand that he considered the dentist who installed my gold crown should have chosen bricklaying for his profession.

After much shaking of his head, he muttered, "Mal, mal, the crown should "stook" as well as "clootch.""

I said, "It already clutches, but you mean it should stick also."

"That's what I said, d'accord. It must stook besides clootch".

After giving me a reproving glance, he turned to open a drawer in one of his elegant chests which an antique dealer in the States would kill for. He pulled out a small silver hammer and began tapping the crown back in place. Thinking my ordeal was over, I swung my legs out of the chair and was about to stand when he pushed me back.

Startled, my first thought was that I was going to be attacked by a French dentist who was the image of the vampire Dracula. Instead, he asked me to open my mouth again and before I realized what he was doing, he'd knocked out the gold crown and was holding it up in triumph like an Olympic medal.

"Voila, regardez-vous comme c'est facile. I told you that it must "stook" as well as "clootch.""

After Dr. Ravier used a combination of glue and hammering, the gold crown was back in its proper place. With great relief, we parted company with as many pleasantries as our fractured English/French could muster. I assured him that I'd see my own "bricklayer" dentist in San Francisco as soon as possible.

Instead I didn't think it wise to tell my San Francisco dentist of my French experience until necessary. French glue must be extra strong because decades later, the gold crown is still both 'stooking' and 'clootching.'"

<u>*Floating Down the Seine*</u>

One hot July day in 1978, our landlady was carefully maneuvering her hefty frame down the steep marble steps leading to the foyer of our newly acquired rental. Madame LaFont owned the converted carriage house at 40 Avenue Georges Mandel in Paris's fashionable 16th Arrondissement, but she herself lived around the corner on the rue des Sablons. Although after today's initial meeting, I'd formed the opinion that location was much too near.

Husband Reg and I had encountered many owners during our years of renting apartments and houses in various sections of France, but Madame de Farge (in my mind I'd already given her that sobriquet) was one of the most formidable. Also one of the most memorable, due to providing me with two unforgettable experiences that summer. This native of Normandy looked as if she'd been assembled from an ironmonger's yard: iron grey hair, iron jaw and steel blue eyes with all her region's noted shrewdness glinting through them. Even her dress was of a metallic grey. She continued to shout instruction over her shoulder as she descended the stairs. "Our agreement was for you to pay Isabella to clean on Tuesdays…don't overpay her; it'll spoil her."

We'd already met the young Spanish woman, Isabella and husband Raoul, who lived in the concierge's quarters. The fragile-looking brunette with two pre-school boys and apparently another infant on the way had looked to me as if she could use a bit of spoiling.

Madame opened the only access to the apartment, a heavy green door made even heavier by its complicated appendage of multiple locks. Her parting shot was, "Monsieur et Madame, always lock *la porte* when you leave, *beaucoup de voleurs à Paris*…remember, if you lock it from the outside, only one on the inside can get out. I have a set of keys and you have another, *mais, c'est tout*, no more keys."

As soon as she slammed the door, husband Reg and I raced to a casement window overlooking the cobblestone courtyard to watch Madame charge across it, pausing only to press a button which opened the massive entrance gates. The gates and our carriage house rental were the only vestiges of the elegant fin de siècle Hotel which had been replaced by a 12 story apartment building.

At Madame's exit, I gave a sigh of relief and said, "Whew, I hope we don't have to see her again 'til we leave. She terrifies me."

Reg said, "Oh, she's not a bad old gal, I think I can jolly her along." I kept silent on my reservations on that score. Although Reg had faced many tough challenges as a corporate executive, I suspected that Madame had intimidated him also. He'd agreed to far more demands from her than he had from previous owners. All cash in advance. Cash, because the French go to such lengths to avoid income tax that it's a wonder any is ever collected.

It seems that she and her late husband, Antoine, had owned an antique shop on the high-priced rue Saint-Honoré. Now she worked out of her apartment and stored excess wares here at 40 Georges Mandel.

We'd also agreed to pay full value for anything damaged during our tenancy, and according to Madame, every item in the apartment was priceless.

"My dear departed Antoine was a genius at finding the best," she'd claimed. It seems that she and her late husband, Antoine, had owned an antique shop on the high-priced rue St. Honore. Now she worked out of her apartment and stored excess wares here at 40 Georges Mandel.

Often in our rentals, we'd received a bouquet of flowers or a bottle of wine as a welcome gesture, but Madame wasn't putting out for that sort of nonsense. Perhaps she felt her information about some of our illustrious neighbors was enough of a gift.

"You know, "she'd bragged, "Princess Stephanie of Monaco lives in the building on your right, and Maria Callas on your left."

Reg had a comment for that. "Oh, yes, she was the mistress of that Greek fellow, Onassis."

Although that remark had reminded me of Reg's distaste for operatic music, I thought that even Reg must have heard of Maria Callas other than her association with Onassis. With some acerbity, I'd scolded, "Reg, the woman was one of the world's greatest sopranos long before she met Onassis."

I jokingly asked, "Do you suppose Madame Callas would loan me a cup of sugar if I knocked on her door?" My feeble attempt at levity had been met with a look of dismay on Madame's face. She threw up her hands and exclaimed, "*Non, non, quelle horreur!* You can't do that, I was assured by niece Marie-France that you were people of character…I wouldn't have rented this place to you otherwise."

After rehashing Madame's indoctrination visit, we concluded that it had contained much useless information; fancy neighbors whom we'd never meet, and a list of untouchables, but little practical guidance, either of the internal workings of the apartment or our immediate neighborhood. We were on our own now.

The first step was a more thorough inspection tour. Pointing to the skylight centered in the high-ceiling living area, Reg remarked, "Do you suppose there's a leak from that when it rains? Maybe that's why Madame's covered so much furniture with sheets. I can't find a place to sit."

Snatching off one of the offending sheets from the long uncomfortable-looking blue velvet Empire sofa, I bowed and said, "*Voilà*, sit thyself down."

Reg gave the sofa a pat and said, "Is this another of Madame's "*ne touchez pas*" items"? She seems to have classed almost everything in the apartment in the 'don't touch' category."

After an experimental bounce on it, he winced and said, "Ouch, this wouldn't even make a good casting couch."

We spent the rest of that day familiarizing ourselves with the apartment and the following few days exploring our neighborhood. Friends often ask in a puzzled tone, "What do you actually do in your long stays in France?" Our answer is that we spend much of the time learning the irregular openings and closing of the various establishments. We discovered that a simple errand to the Victor Hugo post office many blocks away could easily take half the day.

In order to gain more information about the neighborhood and the apartment, I was eagerly looking forward to Isabella's first cleaning Tuesday. Perhaps she could explain some of the secrets of the kitchen. That closet-sized space housed numerous Middle-age relics such as a four-burner gas stove of which only two would light, and a postage-stamp size refrigerator awkwardly positioned against a wall so that it took a contortionist to reach inside.

No dishwasher, washer/dryer or garbage disposal. This spoiled American woman missed the last item most of all. All garbage had to be cut into pieces to fit into minuscule sacks, taken down long steps and across the courtyard to the blue cans, which were usually full.

But my *bête noire* was the oven, which surely had been installed by a King Kong of a workman since I had to stand on tiptoes to put anything in it. Removing a hot dish from its jaws was a test of agility at which I often failed. One evening during our stay, our roast chicken dinner skidded into the living room under its own steam. While I was retrieving it from under Reg's chair, he said he never realized I knew such language.

When Isabella's Tuesday rolled around, Reg wisely planned all-day business appointments away from the apartment. I also planned to make myself dressed and on the look-out for her when she walked slowly towards our door, armed with mop and pail.

After I let her in, a closer look gave me a shock. The young woman looked as if a gentle Paris breeze would topple her to the ground. She staggered up the stairs behind me, collapsed in the nearest chair, and began to cry. I rushed over to put an arm around her shoulder and asked, "Isabella, what's the matter, is it the baby, are you ill?"

Between sobs she told me her problem. Her Spanish/French and my English/French called for much pantomiming on our parts but she communicated that she wasn't ill in body, but spirit. At first when she placed her hand on her heart and said "*Dans mon coeur,*" I thought she had heart trouble, but no, she meant she had a bad case of *mal du pays*. She was homesick for her small village of El Grado in the northern part of Spain where her mother, father, brothers, sisters and even her pet goat still lived. It was making her sick. Husband Raoul had promised that the move to cold Paris would give them a golden future, better than anything in their poor village.

For him maybe, but not for Isabella. I'd already formed a skeptical opinion of Raoul, who was supposed to take care of the heavy maintenance, but the heaviest thing I'd glimpsed him lifting so far was a glass of "vin" with his buddies at the rue de La Pompe BAR-TABAC. Although he obviously had high sperm count, he had a low energy level when it came to such tasks as carrying the blue garbage cans out to the Avenue for collection.

At any rate, this morning when she felt so weak she barely had the strength to button up her navy blue smock, Raoul assured her that her only ailment was *mal du pays*, and if she didn't get her tail over to our apartment, Madame Kearton wouldn't pay her, and Madame LaFont would be furious.

Never mind Madame LaFont, Madame Kearton was furious. This frail pregnant woman, still in her teens, was carrying the burden of two small children, a job, a lazy husband, and she was homesick to boot. Yet, her feverish look bespoke something more than homesickness.

"Isabella, it's temporary with me…I'm homesick too, but it doesn't cause a fever." I felt her flushed face and advised, "I think you have la grippe…go home and tell Raoul to call the doctor."

After paying her for the day anyway and assuring her that I'd clean the place enough to keep Madame off her back with her marine-barracks inspection, she agreed to go home. Her grateful protestations that I not only looked like an angel but was one were accompanied by promises of more work later and candles lit to her patron saint for my protection. She also left her mop and pail as I would need them to keep my cleaning promise.

However, I didn't have to tackle the job at once. With Reg out and Isabella's visit postponed, I elected to have a hot bath in the downstairs bathroom. It would heal my nerves after the morning's encounter. I chose the downstairs tub because the apartment's plumbing system refuted the theory that heat rises. The water was the temperature of a Siberian winter by the time it reached the upstairs bathroom.

Splashing around in the luxury of my first hot bath since our arrival, I began warbling, "I love Paris in the winter when it drizzles, I love Paris in the summer when it sizzles." As I was shouting out a jubilant finish with "I love Paris every moment..." the doorbell rang.

My first thought, that Isabella had made a miraculous recovery, was dismissed immediately, and I continued bathing. But the bell was insistent. "Okay, okay, I'm coming," I grumbled as I climbed out of the tub and ran to peek out of the window. Lo and behold, there was Madame de Farge, who had given up on the bell and was now impatiently pounding on the door with both fists.

Instead of calling out to her, I grabbed a towel and skittered upstairs to the haven of my own bathroom, locking the door behind me. But I hadn't counted on her keys to the apartment. I could hear her stomping up the marble stairs calling "Yoo-hoo, anybody home?..yoo-hoo."

I didn't answer. Instead I finished drying myself and stood quietly with my ear to the door. I could hear her walking around downstairs for about ten minutes before the front door slammed.

I cautiously peeked out of the window in time to see her in the process of locking the front door locks.

The realization that Madame was locking me in for the day unless I could get her attention slowly dawned on me. She didn't have to know of my cowardly flight, just that I was in the tub and didn't hear her. I grabbed my robe from the door hook, ran back to the window, poked my head out, waved my arms, and shouted, "Madame, come back, come back, I've here…you've locked…" The rest of my sentence was silenced by the noise of the gates closing as Madame disappeared from view.

A momentary feeling of panic came over me. The cobblestone courtyard and grey cement apartment building surrounding it had a prison-like appearance which seemed more pronounced now that I was a prisoner; at least until Reg came home. He had taken the keys with the understanding that Isabella would be working in the apartment all day.

The old saying about making lemonade from lemons made me decide to keep my cleaning promise to Isabella. I had an added incentive to sparkle up the place since we'd invited some French friends over later in the week.

Our French friends thought that our carriage house had charm and had given it their highest accolade with the word "bizarre" in the sense of unique. They exclaimed over the mixture of paintings, antiques, bric-a-brac, skylights and shelves lining the high-ceilinged rooms. They were particularly fascinated by the four approximately three-feet-in-length tortoise shells, mounted on stands.

I began by wiping off the tortoise shells and remember how insulted Madame had been when I'd asked if they were plastic replicas. She'd given me a "save me from this Philistine

American woman" look and said, "They're turtles from the Galapagos Islands."

Next I made the sensible decision to work from top to bottom of the shelves so the dust wouldn't fall on what I'd already dusted. I dragged the tall library ladder from a closet, hooked it on the top shelf and climbed up. The entire shelf was filled with grime-coated paperweights of all sizes and colors, with the exception of a special niche which held a Chinese vase. I picked up one of the paperweights and wiped it off with my apron. The stick on the bottom read "France, Baccarat c.1845-50, rose with pink petals; nine green leaves, Base star cut."

Certainly it must be a copy, but taking no chances, I put it back with care and dusted the rest of the paperweights without picking them up. But the Chinese vase needed more attention so I took it to the kitchen for further inspection. When I set it down by the sink, such a cloud of powdery dust rose from it that I had a sneezing fit. It was that and the sight of a spider scurrying around the rim that prompted me to turn on the faucet and give the vase a good rinsing off, inside and out. Like one of those magic coloring books where you brush water over a blank page to bring out the colors, the running water revealed a brilliant blue cloisonné vase decorated with pink flowers and yellow hummingbirds. After returning it to its niche, I continued dusting the rest of the shelves.

For the rest of that week, I prepared for our small party. I filled the place with flowers and potted plants bought at the outdoor market on the Avenue du President Wilson. I also prepared a southern picnic style buffet with such fare as deviled eggs, potato salad and cold fried chicken. The evening was a success. I was getting use to the French crying "bizarre" the minute they walked in the door.

One of the guests that evening was Madame's niece, Marie France, who had been the go-between for our rental. During a chat with her, I remarked, "Marie-France, I invited Madame de Far…Madame LaFont…but she's in Normandy this week. To be honest, I was relieved. She cows me so that I'd probably spend the evening wondering how many "ne touchez pas" rules I'd broken."

Marie France laughed and said, "Oh Françoise, she's really an old pussycat and probably is just as scared of you and Reg."

I gave my friend a look of disbelief. "Well, she gives no indication of being frightened of man or beast…one tough croissant."

Marie France said, "Well, le pauvre bebe, she's been so sad ever since Uncle Antoine's death…they adored each other. Besides, he was the brains of the business…without him, she's convinced she's going to end up sleeping under the Seine bridge."

My friend added, "That's probably why Aunt Yvonne feels it's necessary to squeeze every sou from all her transactions now."

It was two weeks later before Madame and I crossed paths again after she'd inadvertently made me a prisoner in the apartment. But, one day as I was making a grocery list before leaving for the markets, Madame phoned.

"Bonjour, Madame Kearton…would it be convenient if I come by in a few minutes…I need something from the storage closet."

I replied, "Oui, Madame, I'm on my way out but I'll wait."

Hanging up the phone, I walked down the stairs to the foyer and waited at the door. Although Madame had her keys, I was still trying to convey to her that it was "our" apartment for the duration, not hers to pop in and out at will.

Upon her arrival, we exchange greetings and went upstairs. After she'd collected two alabaster lamp bases from the closet, we chatted a minute. She asked if Isabella was doing a satisfactory job for me. I said, "Oh yes, after she got over the flu bug, she's been a big help."

We made our farewells and she'd reached the top of the steps before turning around to say, "Oh Madame Kearton, Isabella knows about the one precious thing in this apartment which she must never touch, but I don't think I mentioned it to you."

I thought to myself that the woman had mentioned so many *"ne touchez pas's"* that one more was incidental.

She pointed to the Chinese vase in its niche on the top shelf and said, "It's so high up that it's quite unlikely you'd ever use that particular vase, but *en tout cas*, never, never touch it for any reason."

Since Madame didn't seem to observe how well I'd shined up that particular vase, I wasn't inclined to volunteer the information that her warning was too late. Instead I asked, "Why, is it all that valuable?"

"Yes, yes, my most valuable and beloved possession." After pausing a moment to pull out the handkerchief from her purse, she explained, "It's Antoine."

"Antoine, what do you mean, Antoine?" I know so little about Oriental art and culture, the thought flitted through my mind that maybe she was speaking of some unfamiliar dynasty period.

She shook her head at my uncomprehending stare. "My dear departed Antoine. Monseiur LaFont...his ashes are in that vase."

Looking down at my feet in the hope that she wouldn't see what must have been my look of stunned surprise, I gave an involuntary groan of "Oh my God, what've I done." She was too wrapped up in her own thoughts to notice and continued, "I can't bear to have his ashes in my apartment, it makes me too sad…but it's a comfort to know that he's nearby."

With those words, a soft tender look washed over Madame's usually stone-like visage and I remembered her niece's words concerning a facet of Madame's character which hitherto had been hidden from me.

"Yes," and her eyes were moist as she said, "I still miss him terribly. You know," she confided, "I never was pretty, even as a girl, but well, Antoine thought I was beautiful."

As if ashamed of allowing me into her private world, she turned abruptly, raced down the stairs and left so hurriedly she failed to close the door.

Dumbfounded, I sat down on the uncomfortable soft for a few moments. Then I looked up at the now empty vase and addressed its recent occupant. "Heaven help me, M. LaFont, you really are the dear departed…in more ways than one."

While I was chewing on my thumbnail and wondering what I could do about the results of my uncharacteristically over-zealous cleaning spree, Reg came up the stairs. His first words were, "What's with Madame…before I could say "bonjour," she went flying by without a word? Did you two have a run-in?"

"No, no," I squeaked, "Reg, I've gone and drowned Monsieur LaFont."

After relating the story to Reg, I sniveled, "Now how on earth can I explain this to Madame?"

Dear Reg, who has rescued me many times, didn't fail me this time. He said, "You won't tell her anything."

He got the ladder, retrieved the Chinese vase, and set it down on the coffee table beside a potted azalea plant I'd bought for the party. He ordered, "Bring me a spoon."

Pulling the plant out of the pot, he spooned the remaining dirt into the vase, returned it to its niche and triumphantly said, "Mission accomplished."

While washing his hands in the sink, he asked, "Is this where you dumped him?"

I nodded yes. After Reg stopped laughing, he said, "I'll bet that's the first time Monsieur LaFont has been out from under Madame's thumb since he met her."

"Reg, you didn't see the look on Madame's face when she spoke of him...a different side of her altogether." I gave him a grateful hug and continued, "Still, instead of being jammed in Madame's antique *ne touchez pas* vase, I like to think of Antoine happily floating down the Seine on a summer's afternoon.

Mr. Big-As-A-Lion

Early one summer morning in 1990, husband Reg and I found an unwelcome note from the manager of the Hotel Jules Cesar in Arles, France under our door. Much to our dismay, it was a request for us to vacate our rooms within two days to accommodate guests with advance reservations. July in such a popular tourist Mecca during the week of its world-renowned Dance Festival was no place to be roofless.

As a result, we stopped by the reception desk to ask the manager if he could find us another vacancy in the vicinity. When later we inquired if he'd had any luck, he gave us the ubiquitous Gallic shrug and said, "Je regrette, Monsieur Kearton, rien pour le moment."

"I regret also," Reg replied. "Please keep trying...and let us know if anything turns up."

We hadn't planned on being in this predicament. Reg had spent weeks carefully shaping our itinerary. As dedicated Francophiles, we'd made many trips to France in the past thirty years. But this one was lengthier than most and arrangements had been made for a roof over our heads for every night of our two months' stay. But, to paraphrase John Steinbeck's observation in his "Travels with Charley," each trip has a personality all its own. The most meticulous safeguards can fly out of the window once the trip begins. We do not take the trip, the trip takes us.

This particular three-week section of our journey was to have been spent in what was described in alluring terms by our San Francisco based rental agency as "a charming four bedroom villa in a beautiful country setting near a quaint village on the outskirts of Aix-en-Provence." Alas, the only feature that matched was the address.

A hasty inspection of the dirty house with its grimy kitchen containing a fly-covered open garbage pail, straw mattresses on the beds, and a Ma-and-Pa Kettle yard filled with rusted junk, all at the end of a long, dusty and barely accessible dirt road, had driven us to the nearest telephone in search of more pleasant accommodations. After several "sorry, we're full" refusals, we were relieved when the Hotel Jules Cesar agreed to take us in for a limited time.

Although we were grateful for the clean bathroom and comfortable beds, the hotel itself had an austere and cold atmosphere harkening back to the days of its original use, a 17th century convent. Upon returning to our room after hearing such discouraging news, the aforementioned atmosphere did nothing to dispel our gloom.

Reg sat down on the side of the bed and said, "Well, get out the old Michelin, we might as well do some sightseeing while we're waiting for news. What looks interesting?"

Leafing through the Michelin, I said, "There certainly are plenty of old Roman stones to see. Provence has more Roman ruins than any place in the world except Italy…I think it has something to do with the dry climate. Let's see…Les Alyscamps isn't a long walk."

"What is it?"

"It says here: 'One of the most celebrated necropolises in the Occidental world, with rows of elaborately carved and decorated sarcophagi on either side of a wide flower-and-tree-lined path.' Hum, the Romans tried to out-do the Joneses even in the cemeteries. The more important the family, the grander the tomb."

"Frances, c'mon, the last thing I'm in the mood for is a visit to a cemetery. At the rate we're going, we may be sleeping on one of those slabs soon. Instead, let's walk to that Roman Arena. We can see it from here."

We left the hotel, crossed the boulevard de Lices, and joined a good-natured holiday crowd on the rue Hôtel-de-Ville. I nudged Reg when a handsome Arlesienne passed by wearing the traditional Provençal costume—a long skirt and apron with a filmy lace fichu and headpiece. In these modern times the becoming outfits are worn only for fête days and pageants, and that seems a pity.

The low hanging clouds spilling intermittent sprinkles of rain were obscuring the famed luminous light of Provence, so loved by Van Gogh, Cezanne and other Impressionists. As we turned right onto the narrow cobble stoned rue Calvade towards the Arena, one of those sprinkles began.

"Let's duck in here 'til it stops," I said, pointing to the door of a real estate office. "We can keep dry at the same time we're finding the perfect place to rent for two weeks."

Reg didn't bother to comment on that fantasy but agreed it was a good excuse to get out of the rain.

The small office contained a desk, a phone, and one comfortable looking middle-aged woman behind the desk, who gave us a friendly smile. After the first "bonjour," she confided that she spoke no English. Reg's French is quite serviceable though, and except for long philosophical discussions, he does well with the basics. In no time he had her sympathetically clucking out repeated ooh-la-la's and *quel dommages* at our sad tale.

In spite of her warm-heartedness, she didn't hold out much hope for a suitable rental but obligingly began looking through her book, shaking her head at each page until suddenly she clapped her hands. "Ah, voila, c'est possible!"

She handed us a fact sheet and said "Monsieur Bigalion called yesterday to say his July tenants were leaving early so he had an unexpected two weeks open until August."

The fact sheet described Le Mas de la Roseraie as a typical Provençal farmhouse on the owner's extensive property located near Pont de Crau, a small village ten kilometers from Arles. Three bedrooms, newly remodeled kitchen and two baths, new innerspring mattresses, television, colorful Provencal furnishings, swimming pool, tennis court and rose garden, all in an orchard setting.

Such a description deserved a look. The agent called M. Bigalion, who suggested that he meet us at our hotel that afternoon. He would drive us to the difficult-to-find house, the understanding that we see the outside only. His tenants had not yet left, but he would show us photographs of the interior.

That taken care of, we were able to continue on our way to the Arena with hope in our hearts. Impressive as the magnificent ruins are, with their reminders of Roman glory from the days before Caesar, they didn't command my undivided attention. I was too elated at the prospect of having our housing problem solved.

Foreign travel doesn't come easily to me even when things go smoothly. Like the local table wine, I tend to turn to vinegar when bounced around too much. I voiced some of my thoughts aloud to Reg. "If the place has a swimming pool and a tennis court, it can't be too shabby."

Reg, ever the pragmatist, reminded me that the description of our last fiasco had read like the Aga Khan's palace.

"Do you suppose M. Bigalion really is?" I wondered.

"Really is what?" Reg asked.

"Big as a lion…that's what his name looks like in English…Mr. Big-as-a-lion. Anyway, it's a good way to remember it."

That afternoon, my question was answered. The small monkey of a man, weather-beaten and browned, who met us in the hotel lobby with a cordial smile and handshake, could by no stretch of the imagination remind anyone of the King of the Beasts. Gnarled and knobby as one of the olive trees that cover Provence, his eyes were his one claim to beauty. The color of the fruit of those same olive trees, a velvety brown, his eyes dominated his face.

We followed him out to his tiny Renault and I prepared to squeeze into the back seat which was filled with bulky parcels. M. Bigalion hastily pushed them down onto the floor, saying that he'd just finished shopping for his dada. For a second I thought he was affectionately referring to his father until I remembered it was the French word for "hobby."

He explained that when he retired from his real estate business in Arles, he and Madame had moved out to their farm which had been in his family for generations. He added that the house we were about to see had fallen into disrepair after his tenant farmer departed, and for his own amusement, M. Bigalion had signed up for a course in bricklaying, as we say, "do-it-yourself." As a result, his hobby had become the remodeling of this farmhouse.

While the two men exchanged pleasantries for the rest of the ride, I settled back to enjoy the scenery.

The mystical look of the countryside of Provence has entranced people for centuries. The melancholy and harsh stretches of desolate hills of white rock are dotted with silvery olive trees and live oaks. The small village houses cling to those hills in a haphazard pattern of faded rose-colored roofs, and are relieved by the thrilling contrast of lush vineyards, gardens and meadows of lavender or bright showy sunflowers, all of which are protected by the long hedges of dark green, aristocratic cypress.

On our arrival, even on this dismal day, we found Le Mas de la Roseraie to be beguiling. It was covered in pale pink plaster, and had the terra cotta wavy roof tiles peculiar to Provence. The first floor was hidden by a trellis over the patio covered with a brilliant fuchsia bougainvillea vine intermingled with the delicate paler purple of wisteria. Blue shutters on four upper-story windows made the color scheme an artist's joy.

The architecture of the house was usual for that region— windows in the front and north walls virtually blank, designed to resist the mistral, the cruel wind which came in winter. The modest-sized pool, set within the front lawn, was surrounded by pink and red rose bushes. We were captivated. For some time we'd had the desire to experience country life in France, as opposed to Paris, for sporadic regional trips. Le Mas de la Roseraie seemed the ideal for such adventures.

While we were signing the agreement in the spacious main house, I was encouraged to see its good solid bourgeois furnishings which boded well for the comfort of our rental. M. Bigalion told us his wife was in Lyon with their daughter who was expecting their first grandchild, but he would have our house in order for our arrival two days hence.

The day we moved into Le Mas de la Roseraie was a hot one. The clouds had moved on and a copper-colored summer sky had returned with a vengeance as if to make up for lost time. M. Bigalion showed us through the house and explained the workings of a wicked, complicated-looking butane stove and oven. He was particularly proud of his tiling work and installation of an intricate shower system in the bathrooms.

He'd hung newly washed linens on the clothesline to dry in the sun. He brought them in and helped me make up our beds. After leaving a bottle of wine and a baguette of fresh bread on the dining room table, he repeated his entreaty that we call him if there was anything more he could do to make our stay pleasant. Then he went whistling off through the orchard towards his hilltop home.

The minute he left, Reg went outside to find a shady place to park the car, and I sat down on one of the dining room tables and began to bawl. And there was plenty to bawl about.

I could begin with the cramped dark rooms sparsely furnished with battered rejects from a flea market; lamps that surely were fueled by anemic fireflies, and spider webs in every corner. The small can of insect spray on the hall table seemed a pathetic weapon against the hordes of flies, bees and mosquitoes which were flying in and out—mostly in—of the unscreened windows.

The winding staircase was too narrow for both us and our bags so everything had to be carried upstairs piecemeal. Furthermore, I was sure to be arrested as a terrorist bomber the first time I tried the stove. If the usual poorly equipped rental kitchens I've known are any example, it's a mystery how France turns out so many world-famous chefs. For me to boil an egg in this lamentable area was going to be a culinary triumph.

I was achingly homesick for my comfortable air-conditioned plastic bubble in California with its clean kitchen, pots and pans that weren't battered and scorched, knives that cut something besides my fingers, and unbroken dishes. But after a few more self-pitying sniffles, I gave myself a pep talk. "Look, you spoiled American ninny, where's your pioneer spirit? Two weeks isn't infinity. We're lucky to have this place. It's an adventure, so treat it like one."

The next few days were spent getting settled. We shopped in Arles at the Monoprix, a French K-Mart, for brighter bulbs for reading lamps, more cans of insect repellent. We learned where the village's best market and boulangerie were and even more important, the various opening and closing hours of those shops, all of which seemed to march to a different drummer. The French are very individualistic.

The first two mornings that I found a tidy pile of fruit by the door, I thought that Reg, who is an early riser, had picked the fruit on his morning constitutional. When I asked Reg to stop picking M. Bigalion's fruit because the pears and apples were hard enough to repair the Appian Way, he told me Mr. Bigalion was my Santa Claus.

I think Monsieur B. was lonesome with Madame away. I was to often hear him and Reg underneath the bedroom window, nattering away over a cup of breakfast coffee. The next time I saw him, I made a point of thanking him for the fruit he'd left and after that, the inedible little pile continued to appear daily.

One morning while walking back from the village, carrying a grocery filled wicker basket and longing for the shopping cart with wheels which I'd left in Paris, I stopped down by the side of the road to rest a moment. A small chicken can weigh like an ostrich by the time you've carried it a kilometer. It was then I saw M. Bigalion across the way, sitting under one of his apple trees and surrounded by an assortment of old clothes. We exchanged waves, but as he seemed absorbed in his mysterious task, I picked up my 'ostrich' and trudged on.

That afternoon on my way to the village post office, he was still under the apple tree, putting finishing touches to his mysterious task. He had fashioned a realistic scarecrow, perched on a small ladder beneath the tree, giving the illusion of a man picking apples.

I stopped to watch him. "Ah, Monsieur Bigalion…c'est drôle…comment dit-on le mot pour 'scare crow"?, I asked, pointing to his creation.

"C'est ca?, Madame Kearton, c'est un épouvantail."

"Well, you're an artist, Monsieur…your work should be in the Paris Museum of Modern Art."

He beamed.

And so the days slipped by. Reg and I explored the countryside, found out-of-the-way places to eat, walked to the village for shopping, and generally adjusted to the slower pace of country life. I even quit screaming—like Chicken Little with her falling sky problem—each time one of M. Bigalion's do-it-yourself bathroom tiles plopped off the wall into my bath water.

It was the shrill ringing of the telephone downstairs at 2 a.m. in the morning in the early part of our second week at Mas La Roserie that first jolted us out of our placidity. Simultaneously, we jumped out of bed collided into each other at the doorway like a Laurel and Hardy comedy scene. Reg squeezed through before I did and immediately crashed in the hall table. While he was recovering, I ran on down the stairs to answer the insistent ringing but it was too dark to see the phone. Just as I located it by sounds, the ringing ceased.

Back upstairs, Reg was hopping around on one foot. After satisfying himself that he wasn't injured, we climbed back into bed. My bed lamp's plug had become disconnected in the excitement so I bent down to plug it in again. As I grasped the electric cord, I almost hit the ceiling. Not only had I received a nasty shock, but in my leap upward, the lamp had fallen over my head. By that time, I was thoroughly awake.

"M. Bigalion must have skipped the course in electrical wiring," I moaned.

After that second shock, I tried to go back to sleep but I fretted that Reg had left the bedroom door ajar. When I got up to close it, Reg said, "Better leave it open…in case the phone rings again."

"But it's so dark in the country," I complained, "and besides, I'm scared. That notice on the inside of the front door says to bolt all doors and windows at night because of the 'vols.'"

Reg tried to reassure me by saying that vols meant 'birds' and added that the birds were asleep by now which was more than he was.

"Reg, I didn't just fall off the turnip truck. 'Vols' may mean birds sometimes, but in this case, the word means burglars." And I shut the door.

The next morning, the plop of another tile in my bath water, the discovery in my bed of a spider large enough to frighten this little Miss Muffet into running out into the olive orchard, and a brief but authoritative belch of flame from the butane oven mangled what shreds were left of my resolution to be a good sport. I called for a family conference.

To my surprise, Reg offered no resistance to my suggestion for an earlier departure date. The previous night's acrobatics had shaken him as well. He wiped a tear from my insect-bitten face and said gently, "Well, sweetie, I'm beginning to agree that this place is too dangerous for a couple of not-as-agile-as-we-once-were senior citizens. I almost fell through the hall floor last night."

"I saw you run into the hall table, but you didn't tell me about the floor. What happened?"

"When I crashed into the table, I found out why Mr. B put such a large table in such a small hall. The base of it covered a hole in the floor a good foot in diameter…the damned hole gives a clear view of the front hall. Anyway, I'm tired of your smelling Citronella Six instead of Chanel Number Five."

After reaching our decision to leave, Reg asked, "But what excuse can we give M. Bigalion?"

"Anything, unexpected business problems a death in the family…which may not be far from the truth if we stay here much longer."

Before Reg went up the hill to tell M. Bigalion of our change in plans, he phoned the hotel near Nice which was our next destination on our two-month trip through France. Upon hearing that we would be welcomed earlier, Reg departed on his diplomatic mission while I joyfully began packing.

About half an hour later, Reg came through the front door. I was coming down the staircase with a load of clothes in my arms since packing involved taking everything down to the luggage still in the living room.

"What took you so long," I said, and not waiting for an answer, added, "I've taken your clothes out of the armoire and put them on the bed."

I made my way into the living room, but Reg kept standing in the hallway with a bemused look on his face. At last he said, "Frances, we can't leave."

Whenever he calls me Frances, it's usually something serious like taxes, overspending, or too much starch in his shorts, so I was all attention.

"Can't leave, can't leave, what do you mean, we can't leave? When startled, I tend to repeat myself.

"Follow me and I'll show you."

I dumped the armload of clothes on the ugly brown sofa and followed him up the hill towards M. Bigalion's house. When we came in sight of it, Reg stopped to point to a flagpole a few hundred yards from the house and said "there."

"What do you mean, 'there?'" I said crossly, bending down to my ankle to scratch my latest mosquito bite.

"There." Reg took my hand and pointed it skyward. "Look what's flying on the flagpole."

I looked, blinked and looked again. At the top of the pole, jauntily whipping in the breeze was the American flag, the Stars and Stripes, Old Glory herself.

Reg explained, "When I was half way up the hill, I met Mr. B. Before I could tell him we were leaving, he said he had a surprise for us and led me the rest of the way to his house. He was as excited as a kid on Christmas morning when he showed me the flag. Apparently he'd visited the U.S. Consulate in Arles to ask them for the loan of a flag for a week…told them he wanted to fly it on his flagpole so his neighbors would know he had Americans in residence. I mean, what was I supposed to do? I didn't have the heart to tell the little guy we were leaving today."

We stood there in silence for a few moments. A yellow butterfly lit on my arm, the same yellow as the sunflowers in one of the meadows across the road; and the breeze that was rippling the flag on the pole smelled of the lavender patch and the rose garden.

"Well," I said, with a deep sigh, "I guess it'll take longer to pack than we thought, say 'til the end of the week?" Back down the hill we went.

We stayed one more day, feeling that was probably long enough for Mr. B. to get his good out of the flag. Reg gave an acceptable excuse of unexpected business problems forcing us to go home ahead of schedule. Men always understand each other when it comes to business problems. Mr. B. offered to refund Reg for the unused portion of our stay, which certainly indicated that his heart was as big as a lion's, even if his physique wasn't.

The morning we left, Mr. B. came down to collect the key and to see us off. He was standing on the patio steps waving goodbye as Reg carefully began maneuvering the car down the narrow lane between the orchards. Suddenly he began shouting to us "Attendez, attendez…wait,wait."

I poked my head out of the window to see what was the matter and saw that Mr. B. had grabbed up the market basket I'd left on the steps and was running through the fruit orchard picking off fruit as fast as he could. Reg stopped the car and Mr. B. thrust the basket of rocklike fruit through the window onto my lap, saying "Bon voyage…for your journey."

Long after such memories as the guide's talk on the glories of the Roman Arena, the marvels of the aqueducts, the haunting beauty of the Provence countryside, yes, and even the heat, the flies and that menacing monster of a stove at Le Mas de la Roseraie have faded, the image of Monsieur "Big as a Lion" running alongside the car all the way down the lane—panting, smiling and waving, reluctant to let 'his' Americans go—will stay with me.

When we pulled out onto the main road, he was still standing there under the big oak with the crooked Le Mas de la Roseraie signpost on it, repeating the words, "Revenez, revenez, come back soon."

And of course we will. Maybe not to Le Mas de la Roseraie, but to France, hopefully encountering more Monsieur Big-as-a-Lions.

Reg stopped to point to a flagpole a few hundred yards from the house and said "there."

Mr. Big-As-A-Lion

That Tugboat Couple

On a fresh April day in 1994, husband Reg and I had been waiting for our New York hotel doorman to whistle up a taxi. Instead of a taxi, a half-a-block long white limousine pulled up to the curb. I nudged Reg and said, "Good grief, look at that gas guzzler; it's bigger than a box car."

My disparaging comments on such an ostentatious mode of transportation continued. "Must be for a rock star and his groupies, or maybe a maharajah's harem…besides," I fretted, " it isn't leaving room for a taxi…that is if we ever get one."

"Surprise, Fran, we don't need a taxi," Reg said with a low bow. "Madame, your carriage awaits."

I looked at him in disbelief and said, "You're kidding?"

"No, no, I decided nothing is too good for a couple of senior citizens taking their first transatlantic sea voyage—and by the way, Happy Birthday."

By the time I realized that Reg had indeed ordered this magic carpet to deliver us to Pier 92 for the QE2 boarding, the driver was standing in front of us. He shook Reg's hand and introduced himself as Hakim. Hakim began the task of loading our luggage into the limousine, a lengthy procedure because Reg and I share a trait of not being able to leave our California home without bringing half its contents with us.

After our four heavy bags, plus briefcases, book bags, and coats were stowed away in the limousine's trunk, we settled back into its soft silvery grey leather seats for the short trip to the docks. After a few blocks, traffic brought us to a jolting stop. Those few minutes of gridlock prompted Hakim to ask "What time does your ship sail? This cross-town traffic can be murder...but at 2:30 in the afternoon...." He let the last sentence trail off and lifted both hands from the steering wheel in a gesture of frustration.

Reg reassured him. "Hakim, we've planned so well that we have hours to spare. We were ready and raring to go right after breakfast. Our itinerary says "QE2—Boarding at 3pm, Sailing at 6pm".

After several more long waits between the stops and starts of this supposedly short trip to our destination, we felt as if our driver Hakim was an old friend of the family. The long distance between the driver's seat and ours didn't deter his continuous stream of small talk. He confided he was a Muslim and he and his wife and two children, a boy, five and a girl, three, lived with his parents. He was an enthusiastic supporter of New York's Metropolitan Opera. To emphasize his love of opera, he pointed to a cage on the seat beside him. "See, I've even named my canaries 'Tristan and Isolde.' They're good enough company while we're stuck in traffic, like now."

As Hakim droned on, Reg kept up his interest in the conversation, but I tuned out by remembering the emotions which prompted me to long for this particular sea voyage. I gave credit to my grandmother, Fanny Maria Topliff Brooks, who died in 1893 at the age of 38. My own mother was eight years old at the time, so I'd never known my namesake.

I'd shown little curiosity about Grandmother Brooks until the discovering of a long-lost box of her letters. The letters covered the four months' tour of Europe she'd taken with her parents in 1883. The family sailed on the Cunard line's SS Servia, the first ship in the world to be lit throughout by electricity.

After reading of Fanny Maria's voyage across the Atlantic a hundred years ago, I had yearned to follow suit. My enthusiasm was contagious because Reg agreed to organize the trip.

While I was mentally thanking my grandmother for this new adventure, Hakim's pulling up to the entrance of Pier 92's shed pulled me back into this century. I was so excited by the sight of the great ship which dominated the scene that I failed to notice the lack of activity normally associated with arrivals or departures of ship sailings. No one greeted us until Hakim blew his horn which summoned a portly gentleman sporting a straggly goatee from a nearby office. He came to the driver's side of the car, peered in and asked us what we wanted.

Hakim said "My passengers are sailing on the QE2 and wish to board."

The portly one had an official Cunard logo on his jacket shook his head and said, "Sorry folks, too late, she's sailed."

To illustrate that devastating statement, he pointed toward the mammoth ship. Sure enough, to our horror, we watched the QE2 slowing easing away from the dock and heard the farewell whistles blasting.

Reg asked, "What can we do to get on board?" The man turned to walk back to the office and said over his shoulder, "Nothing."

Then Reg said, "Well, I'd like to use your telephone."

Obviously Reg's request indicated he hadn't thought of the two limo phones. With the addition of pontoons on Hakim's chariot, we could have crossed the Atlantic in it.

When the man replied, "You'll find a pay phone in the shed," I could almost see Reg's blood pressure go off the top of the chart. Here we'd missed the boat for a very expensive trip and the Cunard employee wasn't offering Reg the services of their office phone a few steps away. I could see "lawsuit" in Reg's eyes.

By then he'd picked up a limousine phone and was calling for American Express emergency when Mr. Goatee shot out of the office. Waving come hither motions, he yelled, "Boss wants to see you."

After Reg had disappeared into the office, I sat in the back seat in stunned silence ticking off a laundry list of jumbled thoughts: no hotel room for the night in a New York bursting with tourists, friends waiting for us in Southampton, firm reservations in England and France. Our careful planning for this six weeks tour was based on five days at sea. That precious five days in the form of the QE2 was disappearing by the minute as it sailed down the Hudson River towards the open sea.

At the moment, my only wailing wall was our driver. I wailed, "But Hakim, it's my birthday! How could that ship leave us on my birthday?" I tended to take events personally.

Hakim interrupted a conversation with his canaries long enough to give me a comforting remark. "Mrs. Kearton, Allah tells me that you'll get on that ship."

124

Fortunately, before I had time to promise Hakim that if Allah was right, I'd convert from Presbyterian to Muslim, I was interrupted by a group of excited people, all screaming, "Hurry, hurry". Reg, plus two men and a woman piled into the limousine with me and urged Hakim to drive to the end of the dock as fast as possible.

Amid the babble, I gleaned that once the woman supervisor understood the problem, she'd called the QE2's Captain Burton-Hall. The captain agreed to allow us to board if a tugboat could overtake the big ship before the pilot boat headed back and if we waived liability insurance in case of injury.

Luckily an available tugboat was waiting for us at the end of the pier. Once there, I realized to my dismay that my mild exercise routine of weekly tap classes doesn't use tugboat-boarding muscles. Without the aid of a gangplank, I had to leave one foot on the dock while putting the other on a much higher narrow ledge and then get them both into the boat. In the process, I looked down between my legs an expanse of water which seemed as wide as the English Channel.

But with the aid of many helping hands, the Keartons and their luggage landed safely on board the small green tug. The Cunardians gave us relieved cries of "Bon Voyage" and in turn received equally relieved farewell thanks. While the tug headed away from the pier, one of the men broke away from the group and sprinted to the limousine. Grabbing Hakim's canary cage off the front seat, he ran to the edge of the dock. Waving the cage back and forth over the water, he yelled, "Jeez, you forgot your canaries!"

By then we were too far away to hear Hakim's protests as he snatched back the cage and restored Tristan and Isolde to their proper place in the limousine.

Twenty minutes later when we approached our ship, I had another fright—the sight of a long rope ladder dangling from the open hold door. I grabbed Reg's arm and said "Oh dear God, do we have to climb up that thing?"

Reg was so busy taking photos of this wild ride, he didn't have time to answer before we were alongside the ship. Much to my relief, our tug's railing was level with the entry way so the rope ladder wasn't necessary. Instead, a crew member threw two orange-colored life jackets onto the tug deck. After donning them, we were hauled aboard like sacks of Idaho potatoes, and escorted to our cabin.

After such a tossing about, we both collapsed in the nearest chairs. In a few moments, Reg broke the silence to say, "I cannot believe all that just happened".

"Well, it did, and if you need any proof, ask those 900 or more people hanging over the railing watching our gymnastics…and no doubt wondering who those idiots were."

As a result of our unorthodox method of boarding the QE2, we gained a certain amount of notoriety during the voyage as that "tugboat couple". My first ocean crossing was different from Grandmother Fanny Maria's in many ways, but I never could have envisioned how different.

In case anyone on shipboard hadn't heard our story, Roger, our Queen's Grill oh-so-veddy British bartender (from Baltimore Maryland) delighted in re-telling the tale to one and all. His last word on the subject came the evening before we were to reach Southampton. He leaned over the bar to say in a confidential whisper, "Mr. and Mrs. Kearton, I've heard a rumor which you should know."

Immediately we chorused, "What?"

Roger studied the glass he was polishing for a moment before saying, "Reliable sources have it that Captain Burton-Hall orders all passengers to disembark in the same manner they embarked...so if you see a tugboat under your porthole tomorrow morning, it has your name on it."

Of course, we didn't believe him, or did we?

The captain agreed to allow us to board if a tugboat could overtake the big ship before the pilot boat headed back and if we waived liability insurance in case of injury.

Sans Plomb

Reg was in the driver's seat and had turned on the ignition of the Mercedes when he heard my scolding voice from the passenger side say, "No, no, I'm not ready. I wish you'd stop grabbing me."

"Fran, I'm not grabbing you, what the matter with you? If you aren't ready now we'll never make Arles for lunch…We've been carless for the three days it's been in the garage. Finally I want us to do some of the things we've planned for this week."

We were about to leave for a daytrip to Arles from Les Frênes, the 19th century bourgoise manor house in Monfavet, a small village near Avignon. Arles is 90 kilometers from here, so I understood Reg's frustration with delays.

But he hadn't understood my complaints. "I wasn't talking to you, it's this stupid car. The minute you turn on the ignition, bells clang and those new state-of-the-art seat belts on arms lunge out like prize fighters or worse yet, car-jackers in the backseat. Scares me silly".

"Buckle up and let's get going before Madame comes out with more helpful instructions."

Monsieur and Madame Biancone were the hardworking owners of Les Frênes and the reason we've stayed overnight with them on previous trips from Paris to Provence. This time we planned a week's stay to explore the surrounding countryside.

With wifely forbearance I refrained from saying "I told you so" for the reason we had been without a car the first three days of our stay.

On our long visits to France we often bought a Mercedes from the Stuttgart factory to drive in France then ship it to the States for a dealer friend to sell in California. Reg spent so much time babying the expensive piece of machinery I wondered if the arrangement was worth it. He said he enjoyed driving the car so much he was willing to risk fender benders plus the problem of fitting a large car in garages meant for small ones.

None so evident as when we checked into a cottage on the grounds of Les Frênes five days ago. As usual the car wouldn't fit in our allocated too-small garage meant only for a mini-deux chevaux the French pretend are cars and drive at heart-attack-producing speeds on narrow mountain roads. Instead, he parked the chariot on the street in front of the hotel. When we got out of the car, I pointed to the electrical wires above us and warned, "Reg, look, the Pigeon Town Council meetings are held there. Best move down the road a bit."

Reg brushed that suggestion aside. "We've had a long drive and we're tired. No problem, the pigeons won't perch on the car."

With an uneasy feeling I saw the wire was crowded now with birds settling down for the night and said, "I'm not worrying about the perching but that other capital P."

He was out of earshot by then so it didn't seem important if the car received a few bird poops during the night, so be it.

That evening we were enjoying an excellent dinner on Les Frênes terrace when I idly whispered, "Reg, why is the woman sitting at the table behind us wearing a fur hat on such a warm night".

Reg said he had no interest in strange women who wore fur hats on a balmy September evening. He'd much rather plan our excursion trip to Arles the next day.

Little did he know that would be a long time coming.

The next morning we had an early breakfast and Reg went for the car. He came back saying the entire car was covered with bird droppings. At times Reg is prone to exaggerations and is a perfectionist so I suspected he meant a few little spots on it. When I saw the car, he had not overstated it. The shiny elegant new Mercedes looked like a piece of Roquefort cheese or an oddly shaped cake with icings.

Instead of our planned trip to Arles, he spent an hour attempting to remove the poop, which by then had turned into hardened cement, etching lovely artistic patterns into the paint finish.

I asked, "Now what do we do?

He used a few unprintable words and dejectedly said, "We ask Madame Biacone for the name of nearest garage and pray this mess can be removed without ruining the paint."

When she saw it, she threw up her hands and said, "Quelle horreur, ce n'est pas bon, ces terribles pigeons. Restez ici."

She said Chef Biancone used the only garage in Montfavet but she had no idea if the owner, Claude Roland, was up to such a difficult task. Perhaps we must take it to Avignon.

We were almost ashamed to drive the car to the village in such a disguise. At least it was a German car, not French.

When M. Roland saw it, he repeated Madame's words: "Quelle horreur! Quel dommage! Qu'est-ce que c'est?"

Reg uttered the word "Pigeons". M. Roland twirled the few strands left on his head and in a sorrowful voice said, "Pigeons, très difficile, très acide."

He said it was a big job but he could do it. After Reg agreed to pay time and half if needed, M. Roland said the chance to work on such a beautiful automobile would be such a pleasure, he'd almost do it without charge.

Then to be certain Reg understood he wasn't serious, he said "Mais, je plaisante vous."

We walked back from the village, relieved the garage was near enough to daily check on his progress.

The first day without a car, M. Biancone invited Reg to join him in a trip to Avignon to stock up on supplies that the small Monfavet markets didn't carry.

With Reg's day taken care of, I looked forward to a leisurely walk to the village to mail letters and visit the florist stands.

The Post Office was next to the City Hall and unlike the crowded lines in the Paris offices, I was the only person at the window. The man behind the grill was dozing in his chair. I've learned how to ask for stamps and fortunately I had all day to accomplish my errands.

Realizing he had a customer, the elderly man rubbed his eyes, looked over the glasses perched on the crook in his nose, and was open for business.

I slid the three letters towards him—two to the States and one to England par avion, and asked for 20 par avion cartes de postales. He asked "Combien?"

I said "Vingt" very clearly, and just to reinforce it, I held up ten fingers twice. That seemed to pin it down.

He then left the window and disappeared in the back and reappeared with the twenty postcards. Next came inspecting the letters. Seven francs for the States, and England a bit less. All had to be turned over a few times, pondered upon and weighed. Again he disappeared to find airmail stickers. Nothing needed seemed to be in a handy place around his window.

The airmail stickers were carefully affixed to the letters in slow motion. I found myself softly humming the tune to a popular song, "A Slow Boat to China."

He seemed quite pleased with the results. He took my money, gave me change, and said, "Voila, Madame, revenez bientôt," and gave me a crinkly toothless smile.

He may not have been as speedy as my Menlo Park post office, but he was a dear man and unlike the speedy ones at home, he was sure to remember me.

Next stop was the small florist shop with buckets of various flowers and potted plants arranged on layered shelves outside the shop.

Usually late summer flowers are not as appealing to me as the spring ones of my April birth date. But the florist had arranged such an artistic display of chrysanthemums in various shades of autumn colors, I couldn't decide between the deep orange and the pale yellow. I chose some of each. Then I spied a pot of red geraniums to give to Madame Biancone for her registration desk.

Second thoughts. Definitely the proverbial coals to Newcastle for someone surrounded by beautiful gardens. Instead, I'll buy a handsome book from one of the Arles museums she recommends.

With my modest selections in hand, I waited behind the only other customer, an overweight pleasant faced middle-aged woman. I'd seen her this morning in the hotel dining room with her even larger and loud-voiced male companion.

She was being served by a young blond man with a wispy attempt for a mustache who looked as if he should be in grade school. As the window sign read "Fleurs et Cadeaux. Gérard et Fils," I assume Père Gerard was giving his son an early start in the florist business. When the woman asked him in English to put her two begonia plants in one container, the florist asked, "Est-ce que pour un cadeau?"

She turned to me with a puzzled look and recognized me also as one of the hotel guests, and asked, "Do you speak any French?"

I replied, "un peu," a little, and explained he asked if the flowers were for a gift. She nodded yes.

He quickly potted them in a yellow straw basket, wrapped it in cellophane, put a sticker and red bow on it, and handed it to her with "Voila, un cadeau!"

On my turn, the same question "Est-ce que pour un cadeau?"

I smiled and said, "Non, le cadeau est pour moi-même."

First he put pink pleated paper on my geranium pot, wrapped it with ribbons and cellophane. Then he arranged the chrysanthemums, added some greenery, wrapped them also in cellophane and an orange ribbon. He worked so fast that he'd finished before I could tell him I was delighted with his work, but did he understand the flowers were only for me.

He waggled a finger at me and said, "Ah, Madame, un cadeau pour soi-même est plus importante que un cadeau pour un autre".

The idea that a gift to oneself is more important than one to another was a new concept. I'll remember the young Frenchman's advice the next time I feel a bit selfish or guilty about buying something just for me.

The Begonia woman had waited for me and we walked out together. We agreed that M. Gerard had no worry about leaving his son in charge of the sales part of the business. Unless Papa thought Son a mite too generous with his ribbons, stickers and cellophane.

Before going our separate ways, we chatted. She introduced herself as Mrs. Elwood Tupper from Johnson City, Tennessee. She said she and husband "El" were on their first trip to Europe.

When we parted she said, "Since we're both Southerners, perhaps you and your husband could join us at dinner tonight. It would be such a relief to talk with people who understand El and me."

Although she seemed an agreeable woman and I empathized with her since I remembered the same longing to be with fellow citizens on my first European trip, Reg would not be pleased with the idea.

At breakfast he'd already expressed his opinion of the couple. He said the man's voice could be heard as far as the village and I had spoiled him for homely plain women. Worst of all, they didn't speak French; Reg likes to exercise his hard-won competence in the language and would not enjoy an evening of southern Tennessee English. My Yankee husband gets enough Atlanta Georgia southern speech from me.

So I excused us with the half-truth of expecting our car from the garage in time for dinner in Avignon.

After we said goodbye, I started home before the flowers wilted in the warm weather without checking on M. Roland's progress. But I did go out of my way to pass le jeu de boules. A few oldish men were playing les boules. If I came back tomorrow and watched the game, maybe I could learn the rules. To me it looked like croquet without the mallets and wickets.

I was having such a good time exploring the village and meeting some of its friendly and to me interesting townspeople. I wasn't in as much rush as Reg to get back on the road.

Nevertheless, two days later M. Roland returned car good as new and we were back to square one with Reg backing car out of Les Frênes driveway for the Arles day trip before Madame could give us more advice on museums to see in Arles.

We had reached the end of the driveway when Madame popped out of the hotel's front door and began waving her arms, shouting, "Monsieur Kearton, attendez!" and pantomimed holding a telephone to her ear.

Reg stopped and groaned, "Dear Lord, hope it isn't a crisis at home."

By then Madame was by his open window with her news. She was still out of breath from her sprint down the driveway when she gasped. "Milles mercies I caught you, M. Giles, the curator of the Muscon Arlanten called me to say it is closed today, but he'll be there this afternoon to give you a personal tour. It's one of the most special museums in Arles. The poet Mistral used his Nobel Prize money to commemorate his beloved Provence."

As fond as Reg was of Madame, it was a gentlemanly effort for him to sound grateful. He could care less if he never saw another museum in this life unless it had something to do with airplanes, space or trains. After Madame trudged back up the driveway, Reg said, "Let's leave before she thinks of any more museums."

At the moment I was attempting to unfold the map so it didn't block driving vision by exploding like a rubber life boat. I'd studied our route last night and so could say with an authoritative voice, "Stay on rue de Montfavet to Avignon when it ends, then a left turn on boulevard Saint Michel for four blocks where same street now crossed boulevard Saint Roche. At the Rhone River a tiny left jog gets us over the Pont de l'Europe to Arles."

Reg patted my knee and let out a sigh of relief. "Sweetie, can you believe we're finally on our way? Claude saved the car from the pigeons and it's perfect weather. After we cross the bridge, what's next?"

Struggling to get the map under control, I found the next step. "Turn left after the bridge on D2, a secondary yellow colored road along the Rhone until Beaucaire. Then cross the river to Tarascon where we connect with N570 for Arles...a piece of cake!"

"Glad you checked it out last evening. We should be in Arles for early lunch with time to visit Madame's curator friend's museum." As the poet Robert Burns wrote, "The best laid schemes o' mice an' men / Go oft awry."

We were on our fourth trip across the world famous bridge when Reg said, "Stop singing that song, it's driving me crazy."

When we first crossed the bridge, I began singing the French folk song, "Sur le pont d'Avignon, l'on y danse" and twenty minutes later was still unconsciously humming it, much to Reg's irritation.

He wasn't so much annoyed by my singing as he was that, after crossing the bridge several times, he invariably found himself on the auto route to Nimes. We could see the little river road underneath the bridge but couldn't find the access.

Time was passing so I suggested, "Maybe we're supposed to go to Nimes today. You may even like it better than Arles. It has some of the best preserved and impressive Roman buildings in Europe."

After another middle of the road turnaround, leaving a chorus of honking horns from on-coming cars, Reg glanced at me in disbelief.

"You, you, who are always such a stickler for keeping promises. What do we tell Madame after her extra efforts on museum dates? That we jilted her for Nimes?"

Better to miss a museum date than have Reg's blood pressure shoot up or have him drive the car over the side of the bridge in frustration. Reg thrives on challenges, but the centuries-old bridge was winning.

Finally, after many illegal turns, wrong way on one way streets, in-and-out of parking lots, we landed on the river road towards Beaucaire.

After I settled down to enjoy the beautiful scenery of the river on one side and the orchard apricot trees with their leaves turning golden autumn colors, I confessed, "I'm glad you stuck it out. This is perfect. SO much better than racing down the auto route to Nimes with no time to enjoy how beautiful France is."

Reg added, "The problem with this country is it would take several lifetimes to see it all. Every inch has an historical story to tell."

We'd been on the road for a few miles when Reg casually observed, "I used up so much gas getting on this road, the gauge is showing nearly empty. At the next village, look for a station with a unleaded gas pump."

I asked, "Does it have to be unleaded?"

"Yes," Reg nodded emphatically. "The instruction book says the Mercedes 560 has delicate innards and only tolerates sans plomb, unleaded gas or the engine will melt."

The first village we came to was St. Pierre Lavemede, consisting of a handful of houses and no gas stations. After we passed three other small villages with no sign of an unleaded pump in their lone gas stations, we realized the sans plomb was not standard equipment, not that much demand for it off the auto routes.

Looking at my feet in their brown dress shoes, I sighed, "I wore these shoes and my blue knit suit in case we go to a posh place for lunch. With no auto club to call and no unleaded gas in sight, glad my walking shoes are in the trunk."

Reg thought there was enough to get us to the larger town of Beaucaire where we were to cross the bridge to Tarascon.

I was comforted with his confidence until the beeps began, an odd noise which sounded like the chirps of a baby chicken. "What's that funny noise coming from the engine, does it mean engine trouble too?"

Reg shook his head. "No, don't worry. It's the engine telling me the gas gauge is low."

The disconcerting beeps continued as a constant reminder that we'd better find gas soon.

When we stopped at an Elf filling station in Beaucaire, still no sign of an unleaded pump. We asked the manager where we could find the elusive unleaded sans plomb. Maybe across the river in Tarascon?

The man shrugged his shoulders and said with pride, "Non, monsieur, nous avons plus ici qu'à Tarascon."

Tarascon and Beaucaire face each other across the Rhone. They aren't enemies but rivals. Maybe it was just civic pride to say Beaucaire had everything Tarascon had and some.

When he said a gas station in Arles 25 kilometers away might have one, I knew he was telling the truth.

All the while the beeps kept beeping and in desperation, I said, "Reg maybe a few gallons of plain old gas wouldn't give this damned car such indigestion it would never recover?"

"No," he shook his head emphatically. "The mechanic warned against such a risk so we'll gamble on Arles."

The car kept reminding us we were about to be stranded any minute. I tuned out by visualizing in my mind the picture of Reg standing beside a green sans plomb gas tank in Arles. When we reached the outskirts, the first gas station we saw had a beautiful green sans plomb pump. I took a photo of Reg with his arms wrapped around it and a big smile on his face.

By then it was too late to find any quaint non-touristy place for lunch, so we ended up at the Hotel Jules Cesar, where we had briefly stayed a few years ago. This magnificent 17th century Carmelite convent was converted to a splendid hotel in the twenties. We were the last people to be accepted for lunch on the. We felt most fortunate and tried not to feel superior to the many poor souls being turned away.

Looking at my pretty brown T-strapped shoes, I said, "I'm glad I changed my shoes. The maitre'd probably wouldn't have seated us if I had been wearing my clodhopper walking shoes."

Reg rolled his eyes and said that was the most ridiculous comment I had ever made. "Surely you didn't think I was serious."

We lapsed into silence until the waiter had served our lunch. Then Reg said, "Fran, something needles me. If the only place for unleaded is Arles, another round trip here won't leave enough in the tank to do much sightseeing."

I gave a look of surprise. "Reg, have you forgotten you were on the nearby auto route to Nimes several times today and all auto routes have unleaded."

"Dear Fran, I hadn't thought of that; we do make a good pair, don't we?"

With that my English reserved partner in life leaned over the table on the terrace of the Jules Cesar and gave me a big fat kiss. I was so startled at the rare and unexpected public display of affection, I almost choked on my salmon. Maybe Reg has some latent French blood in him after all.

We'd spent too much time looking for unleaded gas and a late lunch for the visit to Madame's curator friend M. Giles. Reg called him from the restaurant with apologies, explanations and a promise to see his museum before we left Les Frênes.

That evening while having dinner on the terrace, Madame, who made her usual personal stop at each table, saved ours for last. She was eager to hear if we'd seen her friend, M. Giles, and his museum plus many more of her suggestions for our Arles visit.

Reg began the explanation of our day's failure to add to our knowledge of Arles historical treasures. The more she cross-examined him with rapid fire questions on what we saw in Arles, the more tangled Reg became in his story of the confusing day.

Finally, in exasperation she said, "Mes enfants, just what did you see today? Je ne comprends pas."

By then Reg had given up. So I chimed in and made matters worse by saying "Madame, it's a long story but the best thing we saw in Arles today was the most beautiful green gas pump with the words Sans Plomb on it."

We may never get a reservation at that lovely place again because Madame Biancon looked at the two of us with incredulity. Turning towards the kitchen, I heard her mutter something to her headwaiter Charles that began "Souvent, j'ai dit"…but I didn't hear the rest of the sentence.

I asked Reg what she said. He was laughing so hard he couldn't catch his breath.

Finally explained, "That dear woman said to our waiter, 'See I told you so…all Americans are crazy and the ones from California are the craziest!'

Madame Biancone said, "See I told you so…all Americans are crazy and the ones from California are the craziest!"

Jules César

En Provence, entre Camargue, Alpilles et les Baux,
hôtellerie de caractère aménagée dans un cou-
vent de carmélites du XVIIe, chapelle classée

*After several "sorry, we're full" refusals, we were relieved when
the Hotel Jules Cesar agreed to take us in for a limited time.*

Sans Plomb

<u>Bonne Chance</u>

"One more question, Madame Bechon," I asked in a timid voice. "Is there a taxi stand nearby?"

My timidity was the result of a small contretemps involving a hat and a vase I'd had within seconds after our introduction that morning. Madame was the owner of our newly-rented apartment at 26 rue Surcouf on the Left Bank of Paris. After such an unpromising outset, I contented myself with mutely trailing behind husband Reg and Madame from room to room during the indoctrination period.

My hope that Madame Bechon would be a tad more relaxed about her possessions than our previous Paris landlady of many years had already met with disappointment. I'd labeled our former one, Madame Ne Touchez Pas, among other disrespectful sobriquets such as Madame Defarge, because she'd attached so many Don't Touch notes in the apartment. At times we felt as if we were living in a wedding gift shop.

If first impressions are valid, I feared Madame Bechon wasn't going to be an improvement. She'd arrived on the dot of ten in order to leave extra keys, to answer questions that the concierge who let us in the evening before could not, and most important, to collect her month's rent.

She'd barely shaken the water off her tan umbrella and declined Reg's offer to hang up her damp Burberry—the Paris uniform for June 1991—in the hall closet when she spied my white Panama sunhat perched on one of a pair of tall blue vases on either side of a handsome Louis XVI chest.

Madame Bechon gave me a schoolmarm look and said, "Madame Kearton, s'il vous plait...remove the chapeau, that Sèvres vase is priceless."

I bounded across the room in three long strides and stripped the offending straw hat from my temporary hat stand with such a nervous jerk, the vase teetered a fraction of an inch from side to side—and my heart did the same. Another Madame Ne Touchez Pas, I thought. I felt like retreating thumb in mouth, up the narrow spiral staircase of eighteen worn wooden steps which led to my bedroom for a good sulk.

Here we had wanted to impress her as pillars of senior citizen responsibility. Now she seemed to be having second thoughts about turning her antique filled, book-lined apartment over to a couple of American Francophiles, one of whom was obviously an insensitive klutz.

Her austere demeanor and her barely concealed distaste for her role as landlady softened somewhat when Reg produced the necessary cash-on-the-barrelhead rental check. The mutual friend who had arranged this current Paris haven for us confided that Madame, for undisclosed reasons, was in need of some instant cash. Mine not to wonder why she didn't sell some of her "priceless" antiques and books. Perhaps sentiment interfered with practicality.

Hoping to divert her attention from the hat skirmish, I again asked, "Madame, I may need a taxi this afternoon to visit friend Michele so I'd like to know where the nearest stand is. The closest one to our last rental address was nine long blocks away. Is there a more convenient one around here?"

She said, "Ah, I call this neighborhood, autour le coin, because everything is just around the corner, including the taxi stand. Follow me and I'll show you."

After her good-bye to Reg, whose charm plus check had done a lot to overcome my opening gaffe, we shared her umbrella while picking our way across the slippery cobblestone courtyard, out the green door, past the Chez Wong Chinese restaurant, and up to the corner where rue Surcouf dead-ends into rue St. Dominique.

She waved her hand in that direction and said, "The taxi stand is on the corner, in front of the La Tour-Maubourg brasserie...you can't miss it."

Mission accomplished, Madame shook my hand and said, "I'm leaving for the country today, but Mr. Kearton has my number in case of an emergency." And off she strode down the wet street, umbrella firmly held above her head.

Although she'd left me standing in the rain, her parting remark showed me a burst of sunshine peeping behind the gloomy Paris sky. That meant she wouldn't be popping in and out unexpectedly to check on her Sèvres vases and antique books.

Upon my return to the apartment, Reg handed me the phone after saying, "Wait, Michele, here's Fran now."

Michele, a French friend of long standing, wanted me to come for lunch at her apartment in Neuilly on the outskirts of Paris.

"Fran, I go to Spain tomorrow so it's our only chance to catch up...can you cope with a taxi?"

"Pas de problèmes, there's a taxi stand a couple of blocks away...be there in half an hour."

Michele gave a sigh and said, "Ah, Françoise, ma chérie, I remember when I had to lead you by the hand in France."

By the time I set out on my journey to Neuilly, the rain had stopped but I took an umbrella anyway. When I reached the corner of St. Dominique, I looked over my right shoulder since I'd already learned there was a breathtaking view of the Tour Eiffel from that vantage point. At that moment it was made even more spectacular by the sight of a rainbow, or the musical French word for same, arc-en-ciel, spreading across the sky behind it. I longed for my camera but had not time to retrace my steps.

Madame's directions were accurate, and when I reached the boulevard La Tour-Maubourg, I saw a lone taxi parked at the stand in front of the brasserie.

La Tour-Maubourg is a wide busy boulevard and it took me so long to cross it, I was afraid someone else would grab my cab. The noon rush-hour was approaching and all the taxis whizzing by me were bulging. I dodged a car which jumped the red light and finally made it to the taxi.

At first, I thought the man sitting in the front seat was a passenger. Unlike the more casual attire of most drivers, this one was neatly dressed in a grey suit and tie. My impression was reinforced when he got out of the cab with a briefcase in hand.

"Madame, I may need a taxi this afternoon to visit friend Michele so I'd like to know where the nearest stand is."

The man had a cast in one eye which wandered off to the left, but since no one else was behind me, I assumed he was speaking to me when, with a look of depressed resignation, he asked, "Where?"

"Can you take me to Neuilly?"

A man of few words, he nodded. He flexed the five fingers on his right hand in my face twice and said, "But you must wait ten minutes."

After that baffling remark, he disappeared into the brasserie. I concluded that he was going to have his lunch but wondered how he could eat in ten minutes without having indigestion.

In a few moments, he returned and climbed into the driver's seat. I said, "Now?" He shook his head and held up a fist full of lottery tickets. The mystery was solved.

I sat there in the back seat of the cab and watched him choose his numbers with deliberate care, nothing slap-dash like closing his eyes and letting the pencil fall where it may. After he finished, he gave himself a couple of quick crosses over his chest and returned to the brasserie.

However, true to his word—or fingers, the whole process had taken exactly ten minutes. When we chugged off to Neuilly, I chirped, "Bonne chance".

Why do I always feel compelled to establish some sort of rapport with taxi drivers before I put my life in their hands, particularly Paris taxi drivers? Whether my would-be lottery winner thought I was "good-lucking' him for the lottery or the trip to Neuilly, I don't know, but he answered with a Gallic shrug. That was the end of our sprightly dialogue. When I realized that his route was taking him around l'Étoile, I was happy that we had no more distracting conversation.

The ride around l'Étoile resembles a carnival bumper car game. The French seem to know the rules, but how do they know if some stranger is playing the game for the first time?

"Bonne chance" applied to me as well as my cross-eyed driver. When a black Renault driven by a Grand Prix contender cut us off, making my driver miss his rabbit hole, he muttered "Merde". While we were circling for the second time, I buried my face in my hands and prayed that my last will was in order.

After another thrill-packed drive around the Arc de Triomphe, he headed for Neuilly. He ignored my feeble suggestion on a short cut I knew to the boulevard de la Saussaye, and took the long way around. As a result, when he came to a jerky stop in front of the address, the fare was even more of a healthy sum than usual.

I wasn't acclimated enough to Paris as yet to risk any untranslatable French epithets hurled at me. Consequently I cravenly over-tipped him and climbed out of his death-mobile with relief.

He didn't snarl at me, but there was no "Merci, Madame" as I closed the cab door and started up the path to the apartment house gate. I no sooner had my hand on the latch when I heard the driver call out, "Madame, Madame, attendez".

Startled, I made a quick turn around and saw him leaning out of the window beckoning me to come back. Oh God, I thought, I know I didn't give him dollars instead of francs, but maybe I left something…anything is possible after that wild ride, plus the jet lag I was still feeling.

When I returned to the cab, he thrust a piece of paper in my hand with a "Bonne chance" and drove off with the first smile on his face I'd seen since our short time together.

I stood there staring at the scrap of paper in my hand. What a blooming surprise! The man had given me one of his precious lottery tickets.

I was still shaking my head when I reached Michele's third floor and hoped I remembered the right apartment. No welcome mats for the French, or name plates either. Between a hatred for income tax and a fear of burglaries, they like to keep as low a profile as possible.

After Michele and I had gone through the preliminary affectionate reunion greetings, I told her that the most incredible thing had happened to me.

After I finished my story about the taxi driver, I said, "But Michele, how could I find him? The chances of my winning are nil, but if I did, I ought to share. I don't think he likes being a taxi driver."

Michele raised her elegant eyebrows and said, "Bizarre, bizarre, I never heard of a Paris taxi driver giving anyone anything but the back of his tête."

"Here," she said and snatched the ticket out of my hand, "let me look at that…if it's true, it's a museum piece…you should frame it."

She inspected it carefully and then laughed.

"Oh Françoise, ma petite, so innocent, this is for last week's lottery, so it's no good," she said, pitching it into the wastebasket by her desk.

When I went over to retrieve it, she asked, "Why are you doing that? I told you, it's worthless."

"Never mind," I said, smoothing the slip out. "I'll keep it for my scrapbook. Maybe the fellow was really trying to make up for the long wait, two trips around l'Étoile and the longest route possible here."

Michele rolled her eyes heavenward in a gesture of disbelief.

"Besides," I continued while tucking the expired lottery ticket into my purse, "besides, it is a museum piece. The first time a Parisian taxi driver has ever given me anything—except a bad case of heartburn."

"Ne Touchez Pas!"

Plumbers and Pompiers

Shaking my soundly sleeping husband on the shoulder, I said "Hey, Reg, wake up."

He opened one indignant eye and mumbled, "Wassamatter?"

"In my bathroom, upstairs…water coming from ceiling."

Inasmuch as my first reaction to any crisis in the thirty-some years of our marriage is to holler to Reginald, that's what I was doing. After all, anyone who'd earned all 24 Eagle Scout merit badges in his youth is far more able to cope with crises than a former Campfire girl who never acquired anything from the experience but a severe case of poison ivy.

This time, though, the only response to my crisis call was "Get pails…go to sleep," and then the sound of gentle snoring.

Since he'd shown no interest in what might become the French version of the Johnstown flood, I'd have to handle this one alone.

I stomped back upstairs to my bathroom in our rented apartment at 26 rue Surcouf to reassess the situation. We'd been settled here in Paris in June 1991 for only a few days. Although this latest development wasn't our fault, I was hoping to make it through our month's stay without any damage to our landlady's furnishings.

Madame Bechon claimed that everything in the place was an antique. I believed her because every lamp wobbled at the touch, every chair creaked alarmingly when sat upon, and the place hadn't been rewired since Paris converted from gas to electricity a hundred years ago.

I perched on the edge of the tub, looked up at the ceiling, wiped off a drop of water that had fallen on my forehead, and wished I hadn't made my discovery until morning. Saturday midnight wasn't a propitious time to call for help, even if I'd known whom or what to call.

After Reg and I had returned from a pleasant dinner with French friends, he'd retired to his downstairs bedroom. I'd had a couple of glasses of wine with dinner, so I took extra caution in climbing the narrow steps of the spiral staircase which led to my nest on the upper floor.

I reached the summit safely and began my preparations for bed by washing my face. While leaning over the basin, I noticed that more water was landing on the top of my head than my face. I looked up and saw a sight which had not been there before we'd left for the evening...a foot wide road map of spidery cracks running from one end of the bathroom ceiling to the other, with water oozing from each crack.

The condition hadn't improved since my trip downstairs to share my Chicken Little news with Reg. Now the water dripped in a steady counter-point to the rhythmic sounds of the rain falling outside on the courtyard stones.

The thought occurred to me that someone had left a tap running in the bathroom directly overhead. I ran outside in the rain to see if any lights were on above, but all was in darkness. For a moment I thought I heard whispers, then silence. Who knows, maybe I was interrupting a bathtub murder like the one in the classic French film "Diabolique".

Frustrated in that direction, I followed Reg's pail suggestion. I filled the bathroom with as many pots as I could find in Madame's meager collection, and spent a sleepless night checking the contents every hour to see if they overflowed.

Sunday morning, Reg mounted the staircase to my aerie, looked at the ceiling, and declared that, Sabbath or no, steps must be taken. He called the number in Deauville where Madame said she was spending the weekend. At the bad news, I could hear Madame going into a full scale French version of a hissy fit before she settled down with a practical suggestion. She'd call the pompiers since as she said "impossible, pas de plombier aujourd'hui."

That's another cultural tie France has with the States, no plumbers on Sunday.

At the finish of the conversation, I asked "Reg, why's she going to call the fire department for a flood?"

"I guess the pompiers answer any emergency call. I'd better stand lookout on the sidewalk. Water doesn't send up smoke signals."

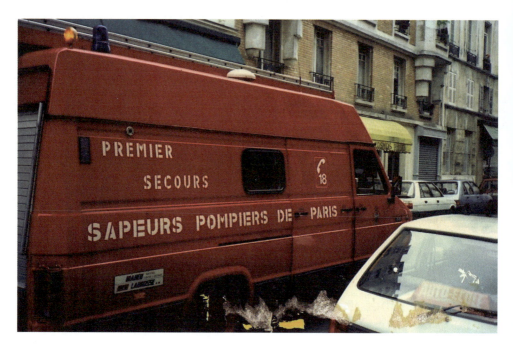

"Reg, why's she going to call the fire department for a flood?"

Reg disappeared out the green door at the far end of the courtyard, and reappeared almost immediately followed by not one or two, but five young muscular soap-opera-looking studs, smartly dressed in navy-blue twill jumpsuits with matching duck-billed caps.

The leader held an official-looking clipboard, introduced himself as Marc and asked the cause of the emergency. I led him upstairs to the bathroom. By that time, the leaks had accelerated to such force that all the pots and pans were overflowing. Secretly, I was grateful for the downpour. If we hadn't had such a worthy display for such a splendid turnout, it would have been most embarrassing.

My guide role over, I retired to the sidelines in a living room chair, and prepared to enjoy the show. The fireman had the same idea I'd had last night—the obvious source must be from the apartment above us.

To gain entry into the empty apartment, a fireman climbed a long ladder and broke the glass in one of the windows overlooking the courtyard.

By this time, the arrival of the firemen and their activities had filled the windows overlooking the courtyard with curious and alarmed neighbors. Marc stood in the center of the square and shouted for everyone to be calm since it was only a minor water leak. Then one irate fellow yelled back that he didn't care about the water leak; he just wanted to know when they were going to move their blasted truck.

The pompiers' red truck was blocking all traffic on rue Surcouf including the access to the garage (fire trucks have the right of way) so we were rapidly becoming well known even beyond the confines of Number 26. Madame later told us that her neighbors found us "charmante". Perhaps that is because we supplied them with so much Sunday entertainment.

Alas, the entertainment didn't discover the source of our Nile, since the apartment above us showed not the slightest hint of dampness. The five firemen abandoned the climb up the tall ladder to my bathroom in favor of a charge up the fragile spiral staircase, which shuddered at each heavy step.

After they had hacked gaping holes in the bathroom ceiling and left tangled masses of plaster and wire on the floor in their fruitless search for the reason for our deluge, they felt they had done their best. Marc apologized for their failure, and suggested we call a plumber as soon as possible. All five firemen shook hands with us and we assured them that we appreciated their efforts.

When the last of the blue twilled-suited men carrying the tall ladder closed the green courtyard door behind him, the show was over. Reg reported the unsatisfactory conclusion to Madame and when he hung up, said "She's driving in from Deauville tonight and will meet her plumber here at 8 a.m. tomorrow".

My face fell and I said, "Oh, no."

"It's okay. The firemen stuffed a lot of rags around the pipes so it won't be as bad."

"It's not the leaks," I protested, "It's her dining room table. Her sharp eyes are bound to notice that it's shrunk."

Reg look perplexed. "Shrunk, Frances? I can't track you sometimes."

When I explained that I'd removed the center extension leaf to use as a bed board, he understood. He has long known my view of French beds. The first night we'd spent at 26 Surcouf, I'd discovered that my upstairs bed held true to form in any of the numerous apartments we'd rented in France.

The beds were left over from World War One, or handed down from medieval times before being discovered in Tante Marie's attic. This time, the Seven Dwarfs dwelled in mine and they were all named Lumpy.

Why every Frenchman isn't afflicted with curvature of the spine is a puzzle to me. Perhaps they are, because you can't walk a block without seeing several discreet brass plaques on buildings announcing the availability inside of a kinésithérapeute. I learned that word the hard way once when I searched in vain and pain for a chiropractor or a physiotherapist. I've often wondered if the profession has a secret factory where they manufacture all the mattresses in France in order to keep themselves supplied with a steady stream of patients.

After waking up that first night in my bed, I decided the only way to avoid turning into a corkscrew by the time we left for home was to find a suitable board to put under the mattress. I prowled around the basement and came up with a couple of discarded cupboard doors, dusted off the spider webs, admired the hand painted designs, and carried them triumphantly upstairs. I was relieved to have solved the problem.

At two a.m. I realized my problem was far from solved. The cupboards had hinges on them which only added hard lumps to the soft ones. Then I thought of the extension leaf in the dining room table. I crept downstairs, removed the leaf and lugged it upstairs without waking Reg. It was a narrow board, and I tended to fall off it during the night, but so far it was my only life raft.

"I guess I'd better put the leaf back in the table before she comes with the plumber, "I said with regret.

"Don't bother. Madame's not going to have anything on her mind but that mess upstairs."

Reg's prediction was correct. Madame arrived at 8 a.m. as promised and was far too concerned about the state of the bathroom to notice that her dining room table had shrunk. She was accompanied by an elderly grey-haired plumber rounded out by so many years of hearty French cooking that he could barely squeeze up the narrow staircase. When he finally puffed his way as far as the door of the bathroom, he surveyed the gaping holes, overflowing pans and tangled masses of plaster in silence.

At last, he threw up his large plump hands and said, "Ooh la la, quelle horreur."

That particular phrase, which I'd not heard anyone use but my French women friends, sounded so funny to me coming from the burly French plumber that I began to laugh.

Madame Bechon looked at me reprovingly. "Madame Kearton, this is no laughing matter."

I couldn't seem to stay out of trouble with Madame Bechon and it was too complicated to explain that I was laughing at the plumber's observation and not the overall situation.

The plumber and his assistant had the leaks repaired and the ceiling plastered over by nightfall. The sequel to this story came a couple of days later. Reg's secretary called from the States to tell us that a carpenter working on a remodeling job for the apartment above ours had driven a nail through a water pipe, resulting in massive water damage to our California apartment.

It was Karma. For the Keartons, no matter which side of the Atlantic we were on, June was "Water Comes From the Ceiling" month.

Plumbers and Pompiers

Mysterious Neighbors

On Thanksgiving Day in 1986, I was scurrying around our kitchen in Menlo Park, California, basting the turkey and tending to last minute preparations for dinner for twelve guests.

As I hovered over the stove, ineffectually un-lumping the gravy, husband Reg bounded into the kitchen with a big grin on his face. "Guess what, Fran! The Chez Vous rental agency says they've found a wonderful Paris apartment for us in the 16th arrondissement for next July."

He clapped his hands while saying, "Isn't that great? We've rented in the 16th before, so you already know where the markets are."

At his announcement, I bent over the reluctant gravy and stirred even faster. Good news for Reg, but bad news for me.

When Reg began business trips to France in 1960 for Lockheed Missiles and Space Corporation, he became enamored of the

country. After he retired in 1975, our trips centered on living in various rentals throughout France for weeks at a time.
Yet, when the novelty wore off for me and my urge to complain surfaced, I restrained myself since I knew rentals were the lesser of two evils. Otherwise, I'd have to agree to Reg's desire to purchase a house with a small vineyard in Provence.

His yearning became a bone of contention between us which was often exacerbated whenever we were houseguests of a wealthy girlhood friend of mine from Atlanta. Anne was also a Francophile and she'd spent a fortune converting a house and vineyard near Arles into a showplace. Since Anne traveled in a private plane with her own staff, I didn't feel that our situation was in any way comparable.

Visions of Reg installing me in a run-down farmhouse, with a few straggly grapevines in its vineyard, chilled my blood. A mental picture of ole Massa Kearton, sitting on the front stoop of a French version of a Tobacco Road shack, saying "Frances, trample those grapes faster," put some spine in my objections.

It was to further cement those Franco-American ties that he and his friend Michele le Menestrel had co-founded the French Heritage Society to begin with.

At first I encouraged the interests but after a decade of keeping house in poorly-equipped kitchens, carrying heavy market baskets up countless stairs, sleeping in uncomfortable beds, and coping with the French language in which, to my shame, I never became proficient, Reg's announcement for the coming summer of 1987 did not fill me with joy.

But on Thanksgiving Day in November, July seemed a long way away, and anything could happen by then.

Well, something did happen. On the first of July in 1987, we arrived in our rented car at 7 rue de la Manutention, only to discover our wonderful apartment was on the fourth floor of a building with no elevator.

How to carry four heavy bags up four flights of stairs was our first challenge.   Fortunately, the Chez Vous agency's Paris representative, Deborah Brady, was a sturdy young woman. She carried the bags up, turned over the keys, and said, "I hope you enjoy your stay."

Deborah fled down the stairs never to be seen or heard from again.   I don't blame her since I wouldn't have the nerve to explain the gaps in the Chez Vous' glowing description of our rental either. Those gaps will be covered in a sequel to this tale.

But this story concerns our neighbors across from our rental. Deborah had failed to mention that the imposing mansion across the street housed the Iranian embassy.   Since we had no expectation of being invited to a neighborly potluck supper, we would have dismissed the news as having no impact on our stay. We couldn't have been more mistaken.

Nevertheless, our disinterest turned into curiosity the morning our apartment's concierge, Madame Roux, delivered the Paris Herald Tribune to our door. Handing it to me, she pointed to the headlines, shook her head and said, "Madame Kearton, la plus ça change, plus c'est la même chose. »

Showing the paper to Reg, I said, "Look at the headline, 'France Breaks Ties with Iran'. It says the envoys are confined to the Embassy and the police are checking automobiles near it. Do you suppose they'll check ours?"

That question was answered almost immediately when we drove our rented Citroen out of the building's underground garage. As our three-blocks-long one-way street dead ended at the steps leading up to avenue President Wilson, our only exit was a left turn at the bottom of those steps on rue Fresnel.

As soon as we'd reached our exit street, a policeman standing on the corner motioned for us to stop.

Reg rolled down his window and asked, "Qu'est-ce que c'est le problem, officer?"

Then he muttered out of the side of his mouth, "Fran, you complain I drive too fast, but this is silly. We've just left the garage!"

Instead of answering Reg's question, the gendarme asked for our passports. After glancing at them, he silently waved us on.

After several days of running this Checkpoint Charlie, we wondered how long the situation would last. Except for the lone policeman, our street stayed quiet with no indication that any international incident was in play.

All that changed the day I looked out a window overlooking our street and yelled, "Reg, come here quick! There's a bunch of men in those rubber wet suits running around the street."

Reg thought I was kidding until he saw for himself and said "How peculiar, they couldn't be scuba divers. The only deep water around is the Seine River, and I doubt any Parisian would go snorkeling in that."

It was later that morning when we had our usual passport inspection by the corner policeman that Reg asked him about the wetsuits swarming about the streets.

"As our three-blocks-long one-way street dead ended at the steps leading up to avenue President Wilson, our only exit was a left turn at the bottom of those steps on rue Fresnel."

171

For once, our taciturn gendarme became more voluble. "Monsieur, those men are experts in tracking criminals trying to escape through the Paris sewers."

"What criminals are they looking for?"

"Mon Dieu, did you just arrive in Paris? The papers are full of the story. Wahid Gordji, the Iranian terrorist, may have escaped from the embassy through the sewers."

Back in the apartment, we read our Herald Tribune with more interest. Until then, except for commenting on that first headline concerning police car searches, we'd paid scant attention to France's problems with Iran.

Upon reading a complex article on the subject, I said, "Reg, I still don't understand. Why don't the police simply go into the Embassy and haul that Wahid fellow out? Beats all this stopping cars, prowling in sewers and keeping us awake half the night with searchlights."

Reg reluctantly laid aside his favorite part of the Tribune, the crossword puzzle, to answer me.

"Okay, Fran, to the best of my ability, I'll explain the situation. Remember when we were in Paris during the Algerian uprising?"

"Of course, the Algerians were supposed to parachute in and take over Paris."

"So you see, France and Europe have been plagued by terrorists for decades so we should be thankful that the USA has been spared. As for the Iranians, France is one of the few remaining countries with diplomatic relations."

I shook my head in puzzlement. "Why the big bust-up now?"

"Because the pro-Iranian Islamic extremists in Lebanon threatened to execute French hostages and try the French consul there as a spy."

Sighing, I said, "I'm ashamed of my ignorance about the Islamic religion or anything to do with the Middle East. I can't even name all those countries."

Reg paused and scratched his head. "You're not alone; most Westerners including me have a difficult time keeping them straight. But this case, the reasoning behind the break is fairly clear. Everyone in the Embassy is confined until they can be sent home."

"Then how do they get food?"

"The one exception is the charge d'affaires, Gholam Reza Haddadi. He's allowed to leave the building."

"Hah," I groaned. "My sympathies are with poor Gholam. I've developed muscles I didn't know I had climbing up and down those 75 steps, lugging home food for just the two of us, much less an entire diplomatic corps. Why all the searching if everyone is in the Embassy?"

"Because the only person who doesn't have diplomatic immunity is Wahid Gordji, the Embassy's interpreter. He's wanted for terrorist bombings in Paris last year. Thirteen killed and more than 150 injured. It's a tit-for-tat game."

Reg has a wonderful ability to simplify even the most intricate subjects for me, so I was beginning to understand our neighbors' predicament. He wound up by saying that France's break with Iran doesn't solve the problem of Wahid. Police can't arrest him as long as he is in the Embassy but like a gopher, the minute he pops outside, he can be forced to appear before a French judge.

173

I said, "That must mean that Mr. Gordji can stay there indefinitely, but with all the others being deported soon, he may get lonely."

That evening before we went to bed, I complained "If they caught Wahid in the sewers today, maybe we can get a good nights' sleep. I'm tired of being stopped each time we leave apartment, and a street filled with wetsuits, and a lot of other inconveniences."

My self-centered wish went unanswered. Instead, around two in the morning we were awakened by the sound of fire engine sirens directly below our bedroom window. Thinking our apartment building was on fire, we bumped heads rushing to the window to see what was going on.

Apparently it wasn't our building, but again the activity centered around the Iranian Embassy. So much fire was shooting high in the sky from the chimneys of the ancient mansion that an alarmed neighbor had called the pompiers. The sparkling embers from the flames resembled the recent July 14 Bastille Day celebration.

As Reg and I leaned out of the window viewing the excitement below, I asked, "Why have those people built fires in some of the hottest weather in Paris?"

"I'd say they were probably using the fireplaces as paper shredders. My guess is that diplomatic immunity keeps the firemen from going into the building unless the residents ask for help."

Reg was correct in his appraisal. The firemen manning the ten fire trucks parked on rue de la Manutention were content with keeping the roofs of the Embassy and surrounding buildings hosed down. Flames, sparks and ashes continued to spew from the Embassy's chimneys until nightfall the next day.

174

A few days before the end of our planned stay at 7 rue de la Manutention, I said, "Reg, have you thought about going home now where our only terrorist neighbor is Mrs. Roger's feisty French poodle? It's ridiculous but sometimes in the middle of the night, I wake up, look across the street and wonder if Wahid has escaped and is coming up our sewer system."

Therefore, with no further knowledge of our mysterious neighbors and with no regrets, we left Paris two days earlier than planned for the south of France. Later we read that in spite of the intense surveillance surrounding the building, three members of the Embassy staff escaped and were caught attempting to smuggle Wahid over the border into West Germany. At last Wahid was turned over to a French judge.

In a false sense of security, it was beyond our comprehension that the United States could ever suffer the terrorist attacks such as France and other European countries have endured for decades. In hindsight, the experiences of our Iranian neighbor that hot July in 1987 were a harbinger of such future events in 2001 as the destruction of New York's World Trade Center, and a part of Washington's Pentagon.

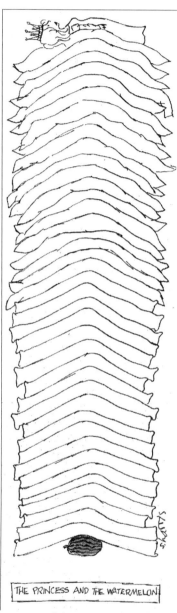

THE PRINCESS AND THE WATERMELON

I think even my mother would agree that I was coping with more than just a small pea under those mattresses!

The Princess and the Pea

In the previous "Mysterious Neighbors" story, I didn't include the cons in Chez Vous' glowing pros of our 7 rue de la Manutention rental. A description of trivial complaints didn't fit into an international Iranian crisis story.

Since the crisis had a fairly successful ending, I can return to carping on French beds as an example of the second part of the book's title, "(And Some I Wish I Hadn't)."

On our many stays in France, of course I've slept in more comfortable beds than uncomfortable ones. Yet in travel experiences, missed trains and ships, lost passports, and stolen luggage mishaps are remembered in greater detail. When travelers return home, friends ask "how was your trip?"

You gush, "It was a dream, it worked out as smoothly as planned."

Notice how their eyes glaze over with a faraway look.

Instead, if you say, "You won't believe this, but it is a wonder we ever got home. We went through check points, ticket takers, stewardesses, etc. with no problems. After we were airborne, we discovered we were on a non-stop plane to Tokyo instead of Turin, Italy!"

Cross my heart, that's another true story. Those two cities had only one thing in common, that they begin with the letter T.

Never mind, you will be the hit of the party. Everyone has more than one travel disaster tale. All will be much worse than my tame bed complaints. So let them write their own book.

The Chez Vous description for 7 rue de la Manutention seemed so ideal, I invited a lifelong friend, Karen Sibley from Atlanta, to visit.

When Reg and I arrived at the address in July of '87, we discovered drawbacks. But there was a big plus: its excellent location, featuring the Museum of Modern Art across the street and the Palais de Chaillot within a few blocks, the Seine at the foot of our short street and two nearby Metro stations, Place d'Iéna and Place Alma.

Nevertheless, in addition to the Iranians, more was unforeseen. In fairness, San Francisco's Chez Vous rental agent, Mrs. Rupert, didn't know there would be an inconvenient international crisis on our doorstep. We won't hold that against her, but she still has a lot to answer for.

The apartment, owned by a young couple with four children, was available because the family spends its summers in the small Normandy village of Livarot, where Monsieur de Moustignas is Honorary Mayor.

At first sight, we felt we had gone too far in our attempts to live in the real France instead of the hotels in superficial tourist tours.

Most of the furniture looked as if every grandmother or relative on both sides of the family had emptied their attics to send it to their kin instead of the French version of our Goodwill second hand stores.

In my realm, the kitchen, every dish was cracked and every knife rusty. Since they had four children, all understandable. I could live with that by buying a few replacements.

In spite of the lacks, the apartment had charm. I'd planned to spend a great deal of time in the nearby Museum of Modern Art, until I learned it was entirely *too* nearby.

The Museum was closed for the summer to install air conditioning. Complete with workmen, scaffolds, air compressing machines, cement trucks, and other equipment involved in a major renovation project. The noise from such activity began at 7a.m. and ceased late in the afternoon, at which time the Iranian activity picked up the slack for the night.

Aside from not being told the apartment was on the fourth floor with no elevator, I based my invitation to Karen on the Chez Vous boast of *three* bedrooms, which clinched the rental. Reg and I have different sleep patterns, so we allocated a bedroom for Reg, one for Fran, and one for visitors.

The brochure didn't lie about three bedrooms, only the comfort therein.

Reg had the owner's master bedroom with a king-sized bed. Reg always offers me the best beds, but he knows and I know that I'll refuse his gentlemanly offer. Unless he sleeps in the best of the beds, I would have to listen to a litany of his aches and pains the next morning. After all, I am ten years younger, so I don't have quite as many aches.

Therefore I inherited the children's room with the bunk beds. My first night I chose the bottom shelf of the bed in the rear of the apartment, as far away from Modern Art noise as possible.

The mattress on each bunk bed was an inch and a half of an ersatz material laid over a wire frame, reminiscent of the Girl Scout Wineemocatchee camps of our youth. So bottom bunk was the wrong choice. Not only did I wake up with wire spring marks on my bottom, I hit my head each time I sat up to turn over.

The second night, I found a clever solution—so I thought. Gathering the four mattresses, which were so light I could lift them with my forefinger, I piled them on the top bunk bed and settled in for a good night's sleep.

While I was arranging my pancake mattress stack, I thought of my mother's favorite sobriquet for me, "the Princess and the Pea." I'd never felt that she meant it as a compliment.

The "clever" solution was a disappointment. The four mattresses sank into a Vee valley which I ineffectually tried to climb until morning. Also, the top bed meant using the ladder each time I left the bed.

If the Moustignas children don't have curvature of the spine by the time they are adults, it's a miracle. I could write a book about French beds I've slept in. Maybe a publisher would think it was a romance novel instead of why I've been under a chiropractor's care for years.

The third night, desperation set in. I was ready to move to a hotel or leave Reg in France. Instead, discovering a futon in the maid's closet, I put it on the floor and slept there for the duration of our stay.

I think even my mother would agree that I was coping with more than just a small pea under those mattresses!

The Princess and the Pea

A Weekend at Fontainebleau

"Michele, I don't want to go to any French country club dinner dance without my husband, and that's final."

"But Françoise, it's the Fontainebleau Club's Spring Dance…you'll ruin my table arrangement if you stay here at the house."

"Oh, c'mon, Michele, unless she's a celebrity, a hostess welcomes an extra woman at a seated dinner like a case of the shingles. I'm doing you a favor."

While on a visit in 1972 to France from our home near San Francisco, I was spending a weekend at Le Clos du Roi, the country house of French friends Michele and Yves de Bonneval. The house was located on property bordering the Fontainebleau forest and near the small village of Recloses. This particular weekend I was without husband Reg, but not by choice. A last-minute business emergency had kept him in Paris.

Michele continued her pleas. "Already I have a very attractive bachelor as your escort. Colonel Boulin will be désolé if you don't come. He loves to practice his English."

Reluctantly, I at last agreed, but I wasn't looking forward to another interminable French dinner. Although my conversational French is adequate for everyday life, it doesn't pass muster at dinner parties. One cannot discuss the weather or the condition of your aunt's stylophone which she left on the table in the garden forever.

Besides I was still smarting from last week's experience of sitting between two French gentlemen at a seven-course formal dinner in Paris when for six of the those seven courses, my two seatmates held a heated argument across my plate on the subject of obscure political candidates in a remote French village.

That argument had continued until one of the gentlemen slammed his fist down so hard on the table the glasses shook, thereby drawing a stern glance of disapproval from our hostess.

When I confided to Michele that evenings such as that were difficult enough for me, even when accompanied by husband Reg, she said with an airy wave of dismissal, "Oh Françoise, this isn't going to be one of those dreary business dinners. These are our friends; it'll be a fun evening."

My objections overcome, I went to my room to dress for the dinner only to find that I had bona fide excuse to duck out. I'd left my mascara case in the Paris hotel.

Back I went to tell Michele that the deal was off. I knew it would be too late to buy more mascara in the village, and Michele would be of no help. With her thick sooty black hair with lashes and brows to match, she had no need of mascara. On the other hand, I'm a fair-skinned blond with pale eyebrows and lashes—a blank white canvas without that make-up tool.

"Without mascara, Michele, I look more like one of the white mice who pulled Cinderella's coach than Cinderella going to the ball."

Michele is a very chic Frenchwoman who always likes to look her best so she treated my seemingly superficial problem seriously. Taking me to her bedroom, she searched through a dressing table drawer until she found a small box. "Here, use these false eyelashes. I bought them once to try, but my lashes don't need them."

Not wishing to upset my hostess further, I returned to my room and began the task of putting on the lashes. I'd often used them in a professional way in years past during a modeling and stage career, but I'd lost the art of gluing them on. At first, I managed to get adhesive everywhere on my face except my eyelids, but at last I achieved the desired glamorous effect.

When it was time to leave, Yves de Bonneval, looking handsome in his dinner clothes, gallantly said he was glad we were to meet the Colonel at the Club. He bragged, "Now I can make a big entrance with a beauty on each arm."

During the drive to the Club, Yves mentioned that Colonel Boulin, my prospective escort, was the Club's current golf champion. I filed that for possible much needed small talk at dinner. And I comforted myself that I had at least one ace-in-the-hole on the subject. In my youth growing up in Atlanta, Georgia, I'd spent many slumber party nights at Clara Jones's house. Clara's father was Bobby Jones, one of Atlanta's heroes, winner in 1930 of four major titles, a feat which brought him enduring recognition as the all-time greatest golfer.

Surely any avid golfer would be interested to know what the renowned man was like in-person. Maybe that would get me through at least two courses dinner-wise.

When we arrived at the imposing Normand timbered building set in acres of lush landscaping, Michele and Yves led the way to a richly paneled reception room with embossed ceiling and leaded windows overlooking a rose garden. A small group of their party had already arrived, including the Colonel. In my imagination, I'd pictured him as a ruddy-faced hearty military type with broad shoulders befitting a champion golfer.

Therefore, while the Colonel was acknowledging his introduction to me with the routine French hand-kissing ritual—a swift pass a few inches above my proffered hand—I hid my surprise at the reality of him, compared to my expectations. With his thinning blonde hair, an elegant elfin face and slender three inches taller than my five-six frame, he reminded me more of Fred Astaire than a muscular golfer.

Why I was surprised, I don't know. Fred Astaire's slight frame managed more unbelievable physical achievements than any golfer ever has. And since I love to dance, I crossed my fingers that the Colonel's fleeting resemblance to Fred included his feet.

After all our party had arrived, a mercifully short time elapsed before Michele indicated that it was time to go to our table for fourteen which was adjacent to the ballroom's dance floor. The French seem to save their serious drinking for the wine at the dinner table rather than the American habit of an extended cocktail hour.

When I found my place card in the middle of the table, far from my two host crutches, a moment of panic swept over me. Now I was dependent for communication on the Colonel on my right

LAST TIME FRAN CAME TO RECLOPES
SHE WEAR A NEW HAT ....
NOV 1ST. 1985

"Avez-vous un flare?"

and a swarthy man who'd been introduced to me as Teddy Nagger of the Paris Egyptian Embassy on my left.

After a few attempts at conversation with Teddy, who spoke French with what I assume was an Egyptian accent and English the same, we abandoned the effort and contented ourselves with an occasional smile.

I didn't have much better luck with the Colonel. I'm certain that Michele had gaily assured him that "Of course Françoise speaks French fluently." Also I discovered that his English was on par with my "aunt's pen on the table" French. And my Bobby Jones ace-in-the-hole folded even before the first course was served when the Colonel said Jones was before his time.

At long last, I was rescued by the orchestra, or so I thought. When they struck up the dance music, the Colonel politely asked me to dance. What a relief—something I could do fairly well with no conversational requirements. After a few turns around the floor, I was pleased to learn that while he was no Fred Astaire, he was a better than average partner. But my newly found pleasure was shattered when the Colonel abruptly drew me closer and whispered in my ear, "Avez-vous un flare?" At least, that's what it sounded like.

Did I have a flare? Or did the man mean did I have a flair for something?

After asking me the same seemingly dumb question several times, and receiving my same puzzled "What do you mean?" answer, he gave up, shrugged his shoulders and escorted me back to the table.

Teddy followed the Colonel's example and invited me to dance also. By that time, I would have eloped to South America with anyone who'd ask me to dance, so I accepted gratefully. Much to my surprise, he continued to follow the Colonel's pattern; a couple of turns around the floor and then the same mystifying query, "Avez-vous un flare/flair?" Whatever. When his third try received nothing but my look of total incomprehension, we finished the dance in silence.

Back at the table once again, the Colonel spoke the first words to me that evening that I clearly understood. Pointing to an area on my forehead, he said in a critical tone of voice, "You have something on your visage which has come unloosed…it need to arrange itself better."

At the same time I was receiving his cryptic message, my hostess Michele beckoned me to join her in the ladies room. Once inside, she said, "Françoise, can't you feel it? One of your false eyelashes is unhooked. It looks like a centipede crawling across your face."

Peering into the bank or mirrors, I realized that "the centipede" was one of my not-born-with eyelashes hanging by a thread of adhesive. Ineffectually trying to glue it back in place, I moaned, "What'll I do? I didn't bring any spare glue with me."

Ever the pragmatic Frenchwoman, Michele ordered, "Take them both off."

As I was repairing my makeup after obeying her, I said, "Michele, maybe you can clear up a mystery. The two men I've danced with, the Colonel and Teddy, have asked me the same peculiar question, "Avez-vous un flair?" How should I know I have any flair, or did they mean a flare you keep in the car trunk for accidents?"

Michele giggled, "Silly girl! They were asking you if you had a lover or 'flirt'. The French pronunciation sounds like 'flare' in

English. If you have style or a flair for something, that's 'éclat', but an accident warning flare is 'fusée éclairante.'"

"If I'd known that, Michele, I'd have told them that I wasn't looking for any flashing lights."

We left the ladies room before I thought to ask Michele if the correct response was a "Oui" or a 'Non". If one answers with a "Non," did that mean she was too unattractive to have a flirt, or that she was available. If so, how seriously did Frenchmen take "flirts"? What were the consequences?

It was a game in which I didn't know the rules. At least now I was mentally prepared to meet a third query with what I felt was a typical Southern tactful response. "Thank you, I already have a lover...but if I didn't, you'd be my first choice."

Unfortunately, I had no more chances to use my newly acquired knowledge of French social customs. Not only did my two dinner partners never invite me to dance again, no one else at the table did either.

Couples whirled on the dance floor, and the unintelligible French conversations whirled around me also. As the evening wore on, I was a small American island isolated in a sea of French babble. I doubt I could have joined in even if I'd had a Sorbonne degree. What conversation threads I did catch consisted of the latest Paris gossip, the latest French cinema-star scandal, and the ubiquitous discussions of current political situations.

If conversational topics are local and filled with inside nuances and references, it doesn't matter what language is spoken. A stranger is lost even in his own native land. I once spent an evening at a Texas dinner party in a vain attempt to follow similar topics of local interest: oil business, Dallas gossip, oil business,

Texas politics, oil...I was no better off there than I was here on this evening.

Finally I became weary of sitting at the table and left unnoticed to explore the territory. Retrieving my light wrap from the cloakroom, I walked down the terrace steps to the rose gardens. The soft night breeze felt fresh on my face after the stuffy crowded ballroom, and a half-moon and lights from inside the building made it easy to see my way outdoors.

My stroll was cut short, however, when small stones from the gravel path lodged in unsuitable-for-hiking satin sandals. Limping back to the terrace, I sat down on a chaise lounge in order to take off my shoes.

Pensively watching the dancers inside, I knew that my first instinct was right. In spite of Michele's assurances to the contrary, this was not the type of gathering to go it alone without husband Reg. Now there was nothing to do but wait until the party was over.

I unstrapped both shoes, pulled my wrap around me and settled back on the lounge. To amuse myself, I began searching the sky for such familiars as the Big Dipper, Orion the Hunter and Pegasus. In the midst of imagining how long it would take to count the Milky Way's stars, I drifted off to sleep.

I was startled awake by a light flashing in my eyes and the sounds of a masculine voice. "Madame, Madame, réveillez-vous. Êtes-vous malade?" Even in my momentarily disoriented state, I understood that he was asking me if I was ill.

Leaping to my shoeless and damp-from-dew feet, I took in the now empty and dimly lit rooms of the club. To my chagrin, I realized that all the guests had departed, and the security guard behind the flashlight was waiting for an explanation from this shivering leftover guest. My mind was so occupied with the task of concocting sentences which would convey my predicament, that I didn't have time to be angry at my thoughtless hosts, to say nothing of my less-than-chivalrous evening escort, the Colonel. The emotions for their leaving me behind like so much abandoned luggage would come later.

At the moment, both the impossibility of remembering the de Bonnevals unlisted phone number and the complicated directions to their house made me think that in spite of the dampness, it would be easier to spend the night on my comfortable terrace chaise lounge. My hosts might not miss me until breakfast, if then, and they had probably assumed that I'd agreed to go with one of my flirt-questioners.

The guard, now impatiently waving his flashlight, repeated his question on the state of my health. As I was stammering out a reply, the French Foreign Legion appears on the terrace in true nick-of-time fashion in the guise of a grumpy, sleep-looking Yves.

Yves explained to the man that Madame had missed her ride home, and that Monsieur de Bonneval had returned to retrieve her. Apparently when the party broke up, I was nowhere in sight, and an attendant at the door told them that the Colonel had already left with a woman on his arm. Mistakenly, the de Bonnevals assumed that said woman was their houseguest, but when they returned home they phoned the Colonel to be certain. It seemed the Colonel had found someone with a more appreciative response than mine to his "avez-vous un flirt/flair/flare?" question.

On the three a.m. lengthy return drive to Le Clos du Roi, the silence was broken only once when I muttered aloud, "All I can say is that Fred would never have left Ginger asleep on a damp dark terrace in the middle of the night in a strange country."

Yves didn't hear me and wouldn't have known what I meant if he had. A fitting ending to an evening of total incomprehension.

Sometimes that's not a bad thing. My uncomprehending response to the puzzling flirt question was the proper one. I don't think Reg, my true flirt, back in his Paris hotel room would have been happy with anything but total incomprehension.

A Weekend at Fontainebleau

Fran and Marie T. on Monet's famous bridge at Giverny.

Checking out the luxurious bath basin at Château de Codignat.

Institut de Français

VILLEFRANCHE-SUR-MER (France)

＊

Certificat

Ce certificat est délivré à

*M*adame Frances KEARTON

qui a suivi un programme intensif de français de 8 heures par jour dans notre Centre

du 29 mars 1976 *au* 23 avril 1976

Appréciations : Elève très agréable, Madame Kearton a réalisé de bons progrès en expression orale où elle a atteint un niveau de correction satisfaisant. Elle a acquis une bonne base qui doit maintenant être consolidée et élargie. Elle doit, en particulier, poursuivre ses efforts afin de développer sa compréhension orale.

Fait à Villefranche-sur-Mer, le 23 avril 1976.

Institut de Français
23, avenue Général Leclerc
06230 Villefranche-sur-Mer
Tél. 80.86.61   France

Le Directeur

I tried to learn the French language, but at the school I was labeled the "white knuckle pupil"…

Southern French

The United States is a melting pot of various ethnic groups, but there is only one France and it's full of Frenchmen. And in May of 1999, during a visit to my native Atlanta, I learned that a Frenchman is a Frenchman no matter where he roams.

When the prospect of having two Frenchmen at my mercy on my home ground instead of theirs arose, I rubbed my hands in sadistic anticipation. After years of prolonged stays in France, now I could speak my native tongue, English southern style, without having my French accent and grammar corrected before I finished a sentence.

The occasion for this small revenge was a board meeting of a national Franco-American organization, The French Heritage Society, co-founded by my husband Reg.

Yet the following incident illustrated that French stories are not confined to France.

On this Atlanta visit, other than seeing some of my remaining lifelong friends, the French Consul's reception in his home on West Paces Ferry Road was a command appearance.

After the five o'clock reception, sixty guests were to be transported to a French restaurant miles from the Consul's house. Our hosts had reservations at the Sainte d'Amour, located in a converted private house on Piedmont Road.

Reg sensibly refused to drive in Atlanta's nightmare traffic and said, "Frances, as a former native at least you're familiar with the street names."

Therefore, in my role of chauffeur, I drove our rental car to the entrance to collect my passengers. In this lottery, other than Reg next to me, I'd drawn three men for the back seat: a New York lawyer board member and his two Parisian guests.

In spite of holding up the line of cars behind me in the driveway, I stopped to ask directions from Barbara Nunnally, a sleek-looking Atlanta woman, who had been introduced as the Transportation Chairman of this event.

When I asked this unlikely elegant traffic controller directions for the Sainte d'Amour, she waved gracefully and vaguely to the right and said, "Keep going on Paces Ferry until you reach Peachtree, then go down Peachtree."

Red Flag time. Atlanta traffic horror stories flashed through my mind. The Bay Area has as many but I'm familiar with the territory and when possible, plan around the hot spots. But since we moved from Atlanta in 1957, that city has morphed from its low-profile Gateway to the South slogan to the New York of the South.

I'd already learned that Atlanta is composed mostly of one-way streets. The only way to get out of downtown Atlanta is to turn around and start over when you reach Greenville, South Carolina.

Uh oh, I thought, when the natives begin instructions with "Go down Peachtree', I'm lost. Do they mean Up or Down?

Peachtree Street has no beginning and no end. It is not to be confused with Peachtree Place, Peachtree Circle, Peachtree Lane, Peachtree Battle and the least fifty more Peachtree-related names. Then my guide said, "You can't miss it, keep on Peachtree towards downtown until you reach a Waffle House, turn right on Piedmont Road 'til you see a grey church. The restaurant is past the church."

Since there are thousands of churches in Atlanta and half of them grey, and probably as many Waffle Houses, her directions left me with an insecure feeling.

Yet even as much as Atlanta had changed since I lived there, I thought I could find Piedmont Road. When the driver in a car behind me gave an impatient honk, I drove off with my cargo.

While Reg, the board member, and the two Parisian gentlemen who'd been introduced as Jean Paul and Roland exchange pleasantries, I drove in silence to better concentrate on the search for the grey church. As I whizzed by the designated church, Roland shouted "Arrêtez, arrêtez."

Apparently he'd glimpsed the discreet calling-card-sized Sainte d'Amour sign at the foot of a narrow driveway.

Then I made the first of many pilot errors; I turned right on the next street, Monroe Drive, which led directly into the mystic Maze of Atlanta's Ansley Park. Ansley Park was the first planned residential section developed in the early 1900's and has kept its original ambiance due to a Park-supported historical organization. But the streets meander in such a confusing fashion that the natives think that the developer, Mr. Edwin Ansley, must have drawn his maps after enjoying too many mint juleps.

Although I'd been born and raised in Ansley Park in a yellow brick house on The Prado, my memory failed me as to how to find an exit back to Piedmont.

After I'd driven past my former house for the third time, Reg remarked, "Fran, we're going to be late if you continue this scenic route with the view of your childhood home."

After Reg's remark, a chorus of suggestions poured forth from the other men. The two Frenchmen hadn't a clue but what they had was the normal French assumption of superiority on any subject including locating a French restaurant in a strange city. I wouldn't have presumed to tell them how to find one in the Bois de Boulogne.

By then I was considering a quickie Mexican divorce from RRK and was ready to sever all Franc-American relations. That decision was reinforced when I overhead Roland remark to Jean Paul, "Quelle d'hommage. La pauvre. Les femmes ne conduisent pas bien rarement."

During the drive, I'd spoken only a few words to the men in my southern English, so perhaps they assumed I knew no French. But I understood them well enough to know of their low opinion of inept women drivers.

When I found my way at last out of Ansley Park, I was still smarting over Roland's remark. As I discharged my passengers at the restaurant's entrance, I couldn't resist having the last word by saying , "Voila, messieurs, nous arrivons sans risque et à l'heure. Je ne parle pas le français couramment, mais je comprends très bien."

Immediately I regretted my smart-alecky retort that their stupid woman chauffeur had delivered them safely and on time under extreme duress. Since that speech taxed my linguistic ability in their beautiful language to the limit, I prayed I wouldn't draw either Jean Paul or Roland as a dinner partner.

My prayer was not answered. The Consul had reserved six tables of ten in the restaurant. After discovering I was seated between the Consul and Roland, I realized I'd been "hoist on my own petard." The Consul said he was delighted to learn that we could have our conversations in French because that fink, Roland, had assured him that Madame Kearton's French was excellent.

Having learned from past experience that if one couldn't speak a Parisian's language flawlessly, the conversation was over, I protested with my standard phrase, "no, no je ne parle pas couramment." That I didn't speak French fluently was the understatement of the year. No matter; the men dived immediately into a spirited discussion on French politics. Every now and then, either the Consul or Roland would look at me and say, "Ah, Madame Kearton, vous êtes d'accord?"

My only required response was to smile while turning my head back and forth as if watching the Wimbledon, and murmur a few soothing "Oui, ouis" of agreement, which sufficed for the duration of the evening.

Suddenly a déjà vu feeling washed over me. I was transported back to the many times in France that Reg and I had clutched illegible directions to some French restaurant hidden behind tall hedges on an unmarked narrow lane. Then, as now, I was trapped in an interminable dinner seated between two Frenchmen discussing obscure points of French politics.

Even on my own turf of Atlanta, Georgia, French restaurants can be just as elusive, and the same goes for conversation between two Frenchmen.

The Marseilles Mafia

One January evening in the year 2000, husband Reg and I were seated at our dinner table in Menlo Park, when Reg announced: "Fran, I've waited all day for the right time to give you good news. San Francisco's recently appointed French Consul, M. Coste, is hosting the reception for my baby Friends of Vieilles Maisons Françaises."

That news gave me a sinking feeling in my stomach, but I stifled a groan and gave a weak smile for his sake. Forcing some fake enthusiasm in my voice, I said, "Oh, great. The name change to French Heritage Society didn't matter, after all your worries."

Never mind my weariness of forty years of dealing with French formal dinners and receptions where my sporadic grasp of the French language often failed me. Of course we must go.

On the reception evening we expected our usual driver, Mary, for our now infrequent night visits to the City. Instead of the smooth-driving Mary, she had substituted Jeff, her son. We'd been exposed to Jeff once before and concluded he aspired to enter the Grand Prix someday. He had a habit of going too fast, then slamming on brakes which made for a jerky ride.

In between the jerks and before we reached the Pacific Heights Jackson Street address, I took out my compact for the fifth time to see if my newly blossomed fever blister on my upper lip had miraculously disappeared. It hadn't, but I hoped my makeup had camouflaged it somewhat, so I asked Reg if he noticed it.

"Reg, why can't fever blisters sprout when you have only to go to grocery store? Instead this one waited until I have to mingle with the San Francisco elite."

Reg said, "Oh, is that what it is. I thought you'd just smeared your lipstick."

His answer didn't bolster my self-confidence, but I knew he had a lot on his mind during this drive.

Reg was looking forward to it because as Chairman Emeritus of FVMF, this reception was the last to honor the original name before merging with other like-minded French related groups and henceforth would be known as The French Heritage Society.

Although I understood his sentimental feelings about the end of an era and how much heart and effort he had put into the organization, I feared the new blood would ignore his contribution.

Those introspective thoughts were interrupted when with a final jerk Jeff stopped in front of the Jackson Street address, and left the car to help Reg up the steps leading to the front door.

When an attendant opened the door, we hit a wall of noise. The noise was caused in some part by too small rooms packed with too many and too large people who had melted into one cohesive group, impossible to walk through.

Undaunted, Reg weaved his way through the crowd to meet the Consul while I lingered at the entrance. After a few minutes of standing alone, two attractive women joined me and began a conversation which, while flattering, had nothing to do with the French. I must have met them before because one asked if I still tap-danced and the other if I had any more copies of my book, Waiting for the Banana Peel. Before I could answer, Reg gestured to me across the room, so excusing myself, I elbowed my way through the throng to join him next to the Consul.

After introducing me to M. Coste and his wife, to my surprise, he whispered "Fran, let's head for the door. I can't stand another minute of this din."

On the drive home, Reg said, "Even though the noise was too much, aren't you glad we went? I was gratified, so many people remembered us."

"For sure. They remembered you. And the Consul urged us to stay so he could introduce you later to the other guests."

Reg said, "I was pleased to be asked, but had no faith in getting anyone's attention. Besides, my main reason for going was to meet M. Coste. We had a good conversation which ended with his assurance of his support for all future French Heritage Society's events."

"Good for him. I like him already but he looked so different from what I expected. Most of the former consuls have had that elegant French aristocratic look. But M. Coste with his muscular build, slick black hair, swarthy face and wearing a red shirt reminded me more of a Marseilles Mafia don."

Reg snorted, "That's a ridiculous comparison. In the first place, you've never been to Marseilles, much less met any Mafia dons."

"Of course I've been...." But I trailed off in mid-sentence, remembering that I'd never told Reg about my visit to Marseilles in the early sixties. My reason being that Reg and I do not always agree on what's hilarious in life.

Besides, the Marseilles visit was his fault anyway. If he hadn't left me for a week at the Carleton Hotel in Cannes, I never would have gone to Marseilles.

One would imagine a week on the Cote d'Azur would be a dream vacation. If all had gone as planned, it might have been. While we were enjoying April in Paris, Jean and Renée Delachair called us there with the appealing suggestion to visit them in Cannes.

We'd met the Delachairs when Jean was in the Lockheed Paris office. But unlike many business associations, we'd become personal friends as well.

Jean had since left Lockheed to return to his native Provence to start a successful recording studio with such clients as rock star Mick Jagger.

The Delachairs not only wanted us to come to Cannes for a personal visit but also for Reg's advice on business problems.

Clever bait on Jean's part because Reg couldn't resist a chance to solve a business challenge.

So the very next day we were on the TGV to Cannes. Before we arrived, I asked Reg if Jean was to meet us at the station. "No, they'll be in Switzerland for a few more days so we can have a wonderful mini-vacation all to ourselves.

Happy news for me because Reg is often occupied with business problems on our French visits. But as soon as we reached the Carleton, that soufflé fell. A message was waiting for Reg which instructed him to leave immediately for Brussels on an assignment.

That message meant that without Reg or the Delachairs, I'd be on my own here in this hotel for several days. After we'd checked in, I looked out at the spectacular view of the blue blue sea of the Bay of Napoule filled with luxurious yachts, the gardens bursting with flowers along the main boulevard, the Croisette, and the blinding sunshine, and realized it meant nothing to me. At that moment such a wave of homesickness came over me, I was ready to take the next plane home to California, or anywhere they understood my southern English.

I asked, "Reg, why can't I go to Brussels? I don't know what to do in Cannes by myself."

"Listen, you'd be by yourself in Brussels most of the time, too. My hotel in Brussels can't compare to the Carleton, one of the best hotels in one of the most beautiful spots in the world. A perfect place for an artist to spend time, so go paint something."

"But, I didn't bring any paints and…" By then I was whining to an empty room. Reg was on his way down the hall to the elevators.

He never understood why I was a timid traveler. He loved going to strange places, eating strange food, and meeting strangers. But I was like a cat in a new place; it took me time to adjust to foreign lands. Looking back on it, I realize now that I suffered from a mild case of xenophobia, fear of strangers or foreigners.

So when Jean Delachair called the hotel to say he and Renée were home, I said "Jean, I'm so happy to hear from you. I was

"Pooh, pooh, Reg can't disapprove from Brussels, and he wouldn't want me to pass up such an adventure."

getting very lonesome. I know the Cary Grant, Grace Kelly movie, "To Catch a Thief" had many scenes filmed at this hotel, but in three days, I have yet to meet anyone remotely resembling Cary Grant, or Grace either."

Jean laughed, "Never mind looking for Cary, Renée and I are going to Marseilles today, could you come with us?"

"For a second, I was afraid you were going to leave me here again. Of course I'll go. I've always wanted to visit the oldest city in France."

"Fran, it's a fascinating city with history on every stone, but I'm afraid you won't have time for exploring. We're staying only long enough to hear an up-coming rock and roll band, "Les Haricorts." I think it wants to be the French Beans answer to the English Beatles."

I giggled. "I like them already, better to be a vegetable than an insect."

Jean warned me that Marseilles was not only one of the oldest cities in Europe but one of the wickedest. The band was playing in a waterfront nightclub "Le Hibou Amusant" so maybe Reg wouldn't approve of my going to such a place.

"Why on earth should Reg object, I've been to plenty of nightclubs?"

"Yeah, but this one is owned by Guy Paillet, a well-known member of the Marseilles Mafia. He's an acquaintance who's been helpful to our recording business."

"Pooh, pooh, Reg can't disapprove from Brussels, and he wouldn't want me to pass up such an adventure."

In case Reg phoned me, I gave a message with the hotel operator that I was with the Delachairs. When they picked me up at the hotel, I left with a clear conscience.

From Cannes to Marseilles is a longer drive than I expected. By the time we reached the entrance of "Le Hibou Amusant" I was ready for bed. But at 10 o'clock, the place was just beginning to come alive.

Our host Guy Paillet welcomed us at the door. While he was leading us to a long table near the bandstand, I whispered to Jean, "Guy doesn't look like Mafia. He's very handsome in a Humphrey Bogart sort of way."

Jean's only answer was a sharp dig in my ribs.

Since we hadn't eaten since breakfast, I was hungry and relieved when Guy said we'd have a late supper after the Beans finished their set.

Much to my disappointment, I didn't have a chance to know Guy better. After a perfunctory civil greeting, he and Jean huddled at the end of the table and began a lengthy conversation. He paid no attention to me the rest of the evening so Reg never had to worry about my being sold into white slavery and shipped to Algiers.

Instead, I had some astonishing attention from a different source. After the French Beans joined our table, I felt as if I'd regressed to grammar school. The Beatles looked like teenagers, but these tender beans looked even younger.

When Claude, the leader, sat next to me, I stifled the urge to ask him if his parents allowed him to stay out so late at night.

Therefore, I wasn't expecting such an active dinner partner. As the evening wore on, no matter how often I moved my knee away from Claude, he promptly moved his next to mine. At first I thought it a casual mistake, but then Robert on my left began squeezing the other knee. And when Jean Paul, who was seated across the table, began rubbing my foot with his toes, I realized that this group of teenagers was all coming on to me. I hadn't had so much masculine attention in years.

I knew that European men look more kindly towards women "d'un certain age" than American men, still this was ridiculous.

I had an uneasy feeling of being the only chicken in a yard filled with roosters. After Claude added hand holding to the knee squeezes, I made an excuse to leave the table before things heated up.

As I passed by the Delachairs and Guy, they were in such deep conversation, no one noticed me. Instead of joining them, I longed to find some fresh sea air. Since the French hadn't as yet accepted that tobacco is unhealthy, the room was so thick with smoke, I had difficulty in seeing the Exit sign.

Once I was outside, I walked across the street and sat on a low stone wall by the ocean. Listening to the soothing slap of the waves against the wall, I decided I would stay there until the drive back to Cannes.

What was I doing here sitting on a stone wall in Marseilles? I was definitely a woman "d'un certain age" because the new rock and roll craze only gave me a headache. And meeting a bona fide Mafia member wasn't that big a thrill. In my youth, I'd met some of his ilk in the States and didn't like them either.

As for having a bunch of testosterone-filled teenagers hit on me, for whatever reason, was only annoying since all I could give them was some motherly advice.

The sight of a man coming out of the club caught my attention. I assumed it was Jean, preparing to leave for Cannes. Instead it was Claude, the Beans leader, who joined me on the wall to say, "Françoise, I missed you."

His English was on par with my French, but we talked some about his ambitions for the band and how he hoped they would eventually be as successful as the Beatles. And if they came to the States maybe he'd see me again.

Then he said, "Françoise, vous êtes très belle." With that, he grabbed me in his arms and kissed me. Not one of those friendly French air pecks on either cheek, but a full scale, you are woman and I am man where do we go from here kiss. Instead of pushing him off the wall into the Mediterranean Sea like an older respectable married woman should, he was such a good kisser, I kissed him back with enthusiasm.

Instead of kissing me again, he turned to point towards a three story building next to the nightclub and said, "Françoise, regardez Le Chalet. C'est très tranquille."

Before I could decide if Claude was pointing to a quaint Marseilles historical inn, or had something more personal in mind, we were interrupted by Jean Delachair.

"Fran, here you are. I was looking for you and Guy is looking for Claude."

Realizing the band's break was over, Claude jumped off the wall. He whispered something in Jean's ear before racing across the street to disappear into the "Le Hibou Amusant" and out of my life.

Puzzled, I asked Jean what Claude had whispered to him that I couldn't hear.

"He asked if you'd recommend his band to your husband."

I said Reg loathed rock-and-roll, so why would he be interested in "Les Haricorts," and in addition, I didn't think Reg would be interested in this Marseilles adventure anyway.

"Jean, I can't imagine why Claude thinks the wife of an aircraft executive would be helpful to their band. That couldn't be why I've had more male attention than since my teenage prom-trotting days. I must be in better shape than I thought."

On the way back to Cannes, the mystery was solved by Jean's confession. "Fran, I asked Claude to be extra polite to you because your husband was the head of an important States record company. You could be a big help in bringing them to the US as a French Challenge to the Beatles. I told them to be polite, not romance you. That was their own idea."

At Jean's explanation, I covered my blushing face with my hands. "Jean, how could you do such a thing? If a person could die of embarrassment, you'd be wondering how to dispose of my body."

Jean had the last word. "Fran, admit it. You had fun and a memorable evening. If I'd introduced you as the wife of an aircraft executive, they would have ignored you completely. As it was, you were the Star."

My mental replay of that unforgettable Marseilles evening came to an end with driver Jeff's abrupt stop, indicating we were home.

While climbing into bed, I said, "Reg, would you like to hear about the time you went to Brussels and left me in Cannes. The Delachairs took me to Marseilles, and…"

By then, Reg was once again sleep. So he missed his last and only chance to hear my Marseilles Mafia story.

French Beds I Have Slept In (And Some I Wish I Hadn't)

Channel Crossing

"Believe me, Mr. and Mrs. Kearton, right now a train/sea Channel crossing from Paris to London is a better bet than air," said Christine, our agreeable American Express travel agent.

At Reg's doubtful look, she continued, "You never know how long these air strikes will last."

The summer months in France are the most popular ones for les grèves, those maddening strikes which make life miserable for natives and visitors alike. A straightforward shutdown of all planes, trains, buses, post offices or other public services would be preferable than this. Some planes may fly, a few trains may run, but which ones and to where remain a well-kept secret.

Christine waited patiently for Reg's decision.

"It's the luggage," he explained. "With four large bags and my broken wing," he indicated his right arm in a makeshift sling, "I can't lift anything for awhile."

"Oh, *pas de problème.*" Christine dismissed Reg's objection with a wave of her elegantly manicured hand. "You can check your luggage through from the Gare du Nord to London."

After we'd settled the arrangements, we walked out to the rue Scribe and headed in the direction of the Madeleine Metro for our temporary quarters, a rented apartment in the 7th Arrondissement.

"Reg, are you sure we can check those bags? I have a vague recollection of having a helluva time years ago when we took the Hovercraft to Folkstone."

Reg had stopped for a moment in front of a men's store to admire a handsome cashmere jacket at an equally handsome price before answering me. "Don't worry, Christine certainly would know a basic like that."

"Look, it's me who'll end up carrying the bags. I think those Copenhagen blue eyes and long blonde hair have made you forget that same Christine had us on the wrong train on the wrong day to Switzerland…remember?"

Reg began pulling me along behind him across the traffic choked boulevard de la Madeleine. "C'mon, we've got the light…besides, we land in Dover this time."

I failed to understand how a change of ports was going to supply more porters. I'd already had a good taste of baggage handling on our way back from a short jaunt to Switzerland the previous week. Reg and the pavement in Lucerne had an unexpected meeting, and he was fortunate to have escaped with only a sprained wrist.

The morning we left for London was a busy one: Keys to be returned to the landlady, hasty last-minute good-byes to friends, and an anxious wait for Philippe, our driver.

218

When we arrived at the Gare du Nord, Philippe left us while he searched for a porter. Fifteen minutes later he returned triumphantly with an ancient blue-smocked porter who must have been the last of that dying breed. The decrepit looking oldster surely wouldn't have the strength to grapple with our bags, which weighed the equivalent of four baby elephants.

But he tossed those bags onto his cart as if they were duck-down pillows, said "*suivez-moi*," and tore off in the direction of our train.

Reg had to run to catch up with him in order to explain that we wanted our bags checked through to London.

"Non, non, c'est impossible."

I think that's the only phrase the porter knew. Accompanied by emphatic head shakes, he repeated it every few seconds during Reg's dialogue. With neither side giving ground, this scenario went on for such length that we began to gather a crowd. Since the station was swarming with nothing but eighteen-year-old backpackers, we stood out with our four huge bags like a South Georgia revival preacher at the Vatican.

At last, the porter threw up his hands and said, "C'est possible, Monsieur, *comme vous voulez.*"

Reg gave me a victorious see-how-persistence-pays-off look. The porter wheeled his cart around preparing to shove off to the freight section.

Over his shoulder, he muttered, "you'll get them in a week or two...*bonne chance*."

Accepting defeat, Reg instructed the victorious porter to load the four bags onto the train for Boulogne.

After boarding we settled down for the journey. For a short while, we watched the French countryside slide by which in the soft July rain, looking fresh, green and inviting. Then Reg said, "I can hear my stomach growling over the train noise, so let's find some lunch."

We discovered there was no dining car, only a snack-booth twelve cars ahead. We made the perilous journey there in time to see the attendant in the process of shutting up shop.

When we returned to our seats, we gave envious looks at the stout German woman across the aisle from us while she unwrapped yet another thick sausage sandwich. Ever since the train had pulled out of the Paris station, she had been chomping steadily on an inexhaustible supply of goodies from her large yellow straw hamper. I offered Reg half of the remains of my chocolate bar, but he said "No thanks, we'll be on the Hovercraft in a little while...I'll get something then."

Upon our arrival at the Boulogne station, a Good Samaritan Frenchman and his muscular young son helped us carry the bags to the platform. Reg instructed me to find a porter while he stayed with the bags.

Since our car was the last one, I had a long hike to the Hovercraft entrance. Several robust handsome young Englishwomen dressed in plain skirts, blue blazers and Scottish Highlander caps with SEACAT COMPANY emblazoned on the ribbons were directing passengers through a minuscule doorway. No porters to be seen.

After three tries, I struck a chord of compassion in one of the Seakittens with my pitiful tale of a hapless husband with a broken arm stranded a quarter of a mile away while sitting on four large bags. I'd already decided a broken arm was more effective than a mere sprain. Before the trip was over, in order to get help, I was willing to break both Reg's arms and a leg.

She found a strapping man behind the scenes, who promised to put them on the craft for a tidy sum. We still had Reg's briefcase, my purse and an overnight satchel to carry ourselves. Reg handed me the cause of his bursitis, his overloaded briefcase, while he picked up the satchel with a groan.

I encouraged him by saying, "C'mon, we can make it as far as the entrance…it couldn't be too far after that to get on board."

And it snows green apples in Minnesota in the summertime, or however the song goes. We inched our way to the lone entrance tunnel, inched our way to ticket taker and thought we were home free when we rounded a blind corner and found ourselves facing four long steep flights of stairs.

While we staggered up those not-so-golden stairs, gasping for breath, I said, "Do you suppose this is something like the different levels of purgatory?"

Reg was occupied at the moment with dodging a long cylindrical object slung across the shoulder of a careless backpacker next to him. When he recovered his balance, he said, "If it is, we'll never make it to the Hovercraft, much less the Promised Land."

Those stairs led us to an enormous waiting room and there we stayed until a voice over the loudspeaker said we could now board. All passengers began to surge up another flight of stairs which led to yet another door, but were stopped mid-flight and told to wait. Apparently the Channel water was so rough, the Hovercraft had difficulty docking.

Forty minutes later, the crowd began to move again. At the top of the stairs, we spewed out of a door marked *Porte d' Embarquement.*

Halleluah, the Promised Land. None such mincemeat. Reg stopped for a moment to rest his arm and a Seacatter said, "Hurry now, sir, or you'll miss the bus."

Out into the rain we went, down a long slippery ramp where buses were waiting. Reg jumped on one but when he turned to grab my hand, the doors closed and the bus pulled away. With no ticket and no money in my purse, I panicked and ran after the bus yelling "Stop". A Seacatter caught up with me to assure me that there'd be another bus soon and my husband would wait at the foot of the gangplank. When we were reunited and boarded the Hovercraft, the woman who showed us our seats realized that by then we were both in heart-attack country.

She said soothingly, "I'll store your satchel and bring it back before we land…and now I'll get you a nice up of hot tea."

Never saw the woman again…or the tea either. When we docked at Dover, we were the last off because we couldn't find Reg's satchel. Why did we keep trusting these people?

When we climbed off that bus I spied two luggage trolleys and grabbed them. We'd need them later. In the meantime, we'd have something to lean on as we followed the serpentine immigration line which moved with all the speed of an over-the-hill caterpillar.

During this long wait, I amused myself by watching the official gate guardian, a rosy-cheeked, mustached gentleman. His task was to direct the flow of traffic through the barricade to the twelve passport-stamping cages. With arthritic-like gestures, he would slowly wave a party to the far end of the row. Then he'd repeat the process for the other end, ignoring the half a dozen stampers directly in front of him.

I pointed out that anomaly to Reg and said, "Why do you suppose he's not sending people to those middle cages—look, that man is inking his stamp pad, the bug-eyed fellow next to him is picking his nose and reading a book…."

"I hope it's a management instruction book," Reg grumbled, "with a chapter on how to overhaul this creaking operation. It must have been set up during the reign of Ethelred the Unready."

I pushed my trolley another foot ahead and asked, "Do you suppose the fellow is nearsighted and can't see those cages with no customers?"

Old cynic Reg said, "No, I'll bet the stampers get a bonus on the number of passports they stamp, and old Walrus Mustache there gets a kickback. The nose pickers are holding out on him."

At last with our passports stamped indicating that we could enter the British Isles with impunity, we went into a cavernous shed to collect our luggage. We were greeted by a sight of acres of luggage with no tags of any sort and no indication of where ours might be.

Again Reg said, "Go find a porter."

That man lives in a dream world, but like a dutiful Lassie, off I raced, made a full circle of the barn and came back with the same answer – no porters.

Reg said, "Stay here, guard the trolleys, and I'll find one."

In preparation for a long wait, I put my purse on one trolley and Reg's briefcase, satchel and raincoat on the other, took out my paperback, and leaned against the wall. I was far away in some other land when I felt a tap on my shoulder.

A tall angular woman, who rather resembled Margaret Hamilton in her role of Oz' Wicked Witch of the West, was standing before me. She spoke to me in one of the hundreds of British regional accents but not being Professor Higgins, I couldn't place it.

"I say there, you don't need two trolleys…you've only got that little bitty purse on one."

I smiled politely and explained that my husband had gone for help with our four bags and we'd need both trolleys. She harumphed back over to her friends, another woman and a man, and the three of them continued to glower at me.

A few minutes later, the woman strode back to say, "Look, we have four bags too…it is very selfish of you to keep trolleys with nothing but a little bitty purse on one."

Since my little bitty purse was the size of watermelon and contained half my worldly goods plus six books, I felt her description was off the mark. I was tempted to lie across the cart and say, "Now I'm on the trolley along with my purse."

Instead I once again explained that since my husband was disabled due to a fall in Switzerland, the two of us couldn't carry four large bags without these trolleys. Why was I relating all this to her? I hate myself sometimes.

Once more the Wicked Witch huffed off. I looked in vain for Reg amid the chaos of screaming people, lost bags, scarce trolleys, no porters and by now not-so-jolly Seacats running around ineffectually.

My gadfly returned immediately—this time with reinforcements. I might have taken on this tall thin woman, but her friend looked as if she'd been stuffing down steak and kidney pies since birth. And they were both prepared to blame me for all their frustrations in life.

The sumo wrestler woman grabbed my little bitty purse trolley and announced, "We have four bags too...I have a heart condition and we're taking this trolley."

No more smiling from me. By then I'd had it. I said, "We all have problems. I've pushed these trolleys since infinity, we need them and that's that. If you don't leave me alone, I'm calling for help."

The sumo woman let go of the trolley, but the Witch grabbed it again. I started yelling at the top of my lungs. I'd only gotten out one loud "Police" when the pair fled.

At long last, Reg returned with a baggage department man who found our bags, loaded them onto the two trolleys and said, "Where to?"

At that moment one of the Seacat women came up to us and said, "Hurry up now, you'll miss the bus."

Apparently we were in one of those Nintendo games called Mazes and Monsters. This entire mad teeming horde of people with luggage was to be once again jammed on buses to be taken to the Dover train station.

I looked at Reg and , "Bus, bus, bus...no way Jose am I getting on another bus. Taxi, taxi, taxi."

We arrived at the station before the crowd. No porters, but a taxi driver got us up the three flights of stairs to the platform. We piled into a train which was leaving immediately for London. Never mind that it was the wrong train for our tickets and stopped at every Three Crowns, Upper Ipswich and Lower Farthingham station en route. We were happy to be on it.

When we arrived at Victoria Station, our driver had long since given up on us. We hailed a taxi and fell into our hotel around midnight.

We collapsed on the bed and lay there for awhile, too tired to undress. Finally Reg looked at me with half closed eyes and said, "an unspeakable thought has occurred to me...do you remember that our plane to San Francisco leaves from the *Paris* airport?"

I stirred myself long enough to get up and walk over to the window. I yawned and said, "So what, strikes are sure to be over by next week."

"You don't get it Fran. I bought round trip tickets for the Hovercraft. Now I know what "to hell and back" really means."

I stood there silently looking down on the Park street traffic. The rain had stopped but the black London cabs, cars and street were still wet and shimmering.

Finally I said, "Reg, I don't think it'll be so hard for me to get used to English weather...and when you get home, you can just send me my clothes."

By the Time We Get to Phoenix

One early April morning in 2001, I waved goodbye to Reg as he headed towards the stairs to the garage. Before he disappeared from view, I yelled, "Reg, don't forget to ask Dr. Sarah if you can fly to Phoenix."

Reg testily yelled back, "Fran, the heart surgery was a success. Of course we'll go to Phoenix next week. And stop screaming at me like a fishwife, you'll wake the neighbors."

Fishwife or no, with a hard-of-hearing obstinate ninety-year-old, sometimes shouting to get his attention was preferable to hitting him on the nose with a two-by-four like a stubborn mule.

Before his recent heart surgery, Reg had planned to attend a French Heritage Society board meeting to add the newly-formed Arizona chapter to the existing 15 chapters in the United States. A co-founder and Chairman Emeritus, Reg was still active in the organization.

Phoenix was a long way from France, but perhaps the hot desert weather there made the members long for the fresh green fields of the French countryside.

Mine not to reason why Reg's French involvement was going to land us in one of the hottest parts of the country…yet I had spent many times in France when the only relief from the heat was to sit in a tub of cool water.

In my secret heart I hoped Dr. Sarah would not approve of such strenuous travel so soon after his surgery. And when Reg returned home, he looked so downcast I thought my wish had been granted. In reply to my questioning look, he grumbled, "She says too soon to fly, some cockamamie risk of blood clots."

In a way I was relieved, but when he began canceling Phoenix hotel reservations, he looked so dejected that out of my mouth came this impulsive suggestion. "If you can't fly, why don't we drive to Phoenix?"

Reg's face lit up as though he had won the lottery. As a former aircraft executive, he's spent so many years of air travel, sometimes he forgot that there are other modes of transportation. "Fran, we'd miss the wheelchairs, the cancelled flights, no porters. Great idea, and you can plan the road trip."

With my suggestion, I was hoisted on my own petard. I spent several days poring over the maps and the Automobile Association's books for routes and lodgings. While doing so, I found myself humming over and over the Glen Campbell song, "By the Time I Get to Phoenix."

I have doubts the man ever reached Phoenix by his odd route, no matter where he began his journey. Perhaps the notes he left his girl, first from Albuquerque then east to Oklahoma, would more likely land him in New Jersey than Phoenix.

As for me, my main objective was to plan a route to Phoenix that, no matter how convoluted, avoided that Gateway to Hell known as the Los Angeles freeway system.

April 23. Monterey was our first stop because of Reg's appointment with his dermatologist, Dr. Rheim. Then on to Visalia, Barstow, Blythe, and Phoenix. Those dry, dusty small towns, interspersed with long stretches of desert, were not a scenic route, but I had never seen that section of California, so I kept a journal of my impressions.

Day one, we arrived in Monterey in time for lunch at one of the most beautiful spots in the world, the Pebble Beach Golf and Tennis Club. We spent the night at the Seaside Embassy Suites with dinner in their Pacific restaurant. We watched the fish swimming in the aquarium around the walls and felt that we were off to a swimmingly good beginning.

April 24, my birthday, wherein I received an unexpected but appreciated gift. After Reg's visit, Dr. Rheim came out with him and gave me a hug.

Dr. Rheim is an expert in dealing with Reg's cancer-prone redhead skin; he is also a pleasure to visit. He is an extrovert, and with his Italian heritage good looks, he could play the lead in any TV show. After the brief hug, he gave my face a closer look and began poking his finger on a small pimple beside my nose. "Fran, how long have you had this?"

I answered "Weeks, and yet it doesn't seem to heal."

Before I knew it, I was in his treatment room's reclining chair while the doctor dug a small but deep hole in my face. "Fran, it's a basal carcinoma skin cancer, and I'm glad we caught it early. Don't worry, the scar will fade soon."

Reassuring words. A blemish on my face drives me crazy, a hangover from earning my living for so long in the fashion and TV business, both pursuits depending on physical image. A lucky present, too, because I probably would have waited weeks before going to a doctor.

Reg drove as far as King City, where we had lunch. Then he said I could drive to Visalia, our night's destination. I turned off 101 onto route 198 in Coalinga to reach route 99 to Visalia. Thank God I was driving. I'd taken that hilly, winding road years ago and remembered its beautiful, unspoiled scenery. But I don't recall it being so long. Fifty miles to reach 99 with Himself complaining all the way.

He kept asking, "Who chose this rough road?" Since there were only two people in the car, not a difficult question to answer.

Fortunately, our Visalia motel, the LampLighters, was charming. A cottage with roses in front. Staff helpful. Smaller towns seem to produce more of that attitude. The coffee shop restaurant next door, Sneaker's Sports Bar and Grill, was the locale for my birthday dinner.

For me, it was perfect. There were only a few people in the Grill; most of the other customers were in the bar on the other side. Reg tried to order a cupcake with candles, but our blonde waitress/owner said she didn't have any candles or cupcakes either.

For some reason, that upset him. Why, I don't know. It was my birthday. I was happy with a quiet booth, a glass of wine, and some of the best fried chicken I've had since leaving Georgia.

The only complaint in our living room/bedroom cottage was that there were NO READING LAMPS on the bedside table. The first time in all our travels that we've been in a hotel that didn't have that necessity! I solved the problem with my travel extension cord and moved a living room lamp into the bedroom.

So, in a way, I'll remember my 81st birthday more than some of the others.

Wednesday, April 25. On the way to Barstow for our next night's stay, I was the driver over the wicked Tehachapi Pass. When we reached the town of Tehachapi (pop. 5,800, elev 3,970'), I had gripped the wheel so tightly, Reg had to pry my hands off of it.

After I had taken several deep breaths of relief, Reg said "Fran, you did a great job of getting over those mountains. You are a really good driver." Reg's father was a rather reserved Englishman, so I attributed Reg's scarcity of compliments to his heritage. Hence, when I get one, I know he means it and I treasure it. But just as I was puffing up a tad, he added the qualification "for a woman."

But I didn't spend several years in an early live ad-lib TV show with a now famous comedian, Dick Van Dyke, without a comeback of my own.

"Sweetie, I appreciate the compliment. You are also an excellent driver—for a man."

Never mind who was a good driver, we got there with no mishaps and were now hungry for lunch. There were very few eating places in the town, and the Best Western Mountain Inn seemed the best choice…

We parked between two motorcycles. This, I realized later, was a portent of future events. Scenes of Hitchcock's *The Birds* come to mind. A Birds and Bikers connect was not as unlikely as one would think, as overwhelmingly large flocks of either are frightening.

After we settled in a booth, a waitress wearing a train engineer's cap took our order. When she left, I commented, "I wonder why the train motif instead of a prison one. I thought Tehachapi's only feature was the women's prison, or the kinder term Women's Correctional Facility."

The waitress left a boxcar-shaped bread basket, so I helped myself to a biscuit and continued my observation. "Well, trains are more cheerful than prisons, but still a mystery."

My aeronautical engineer husband said, "There's more to this area than a prison. Didn't you see those wind turbines when we went over the mountains?"

"I was too busy driving to see anything but which one of those scary curves was coming up next."

Reg explained that the old railroad town in the Tehachapi Mountains is now known as the Tehachapi-Mojave Wind Resource Area. The turbines we passed generate 1.3 billion kilowatt hours of electricity a year.

I replied "Wow, maybe we could take one home for our rolling blackout days. But what do turbines and prisons have to do with toy trains, photos, and the help dressed up like engineers or conductors?"

My question was answered on the way out, when we walked past a model railway exhibit of the Tehachapi Loop. The plaque explained that the Loop was conceived by a railroad engineer in 1976 to surmount a steep grade. It enables the last car of at an 85-car train to pass above the engine in the tunnel below.

The plaque didn't mention the name of the clever engineer who conceived the idea. So many unrecognized talents in this world, and so many recognized no-talents, a puzzlement.

After leaving Tehachapi with Reg at the wheel, we continued on Route 40 to Barstow. On the way, he asked "Where do we stay tonight?"

I opened our AAA tour book and said, "Not much choice. I booked us in the only three-star listed, the Best Western Desert Villa Inn. Their ad description sounds promising: 'Make your desert stay a truly restful stop. Newly renovated rooms, centrally located between Las Vegas and Los Angeles, near Barstow shopping mall' and so forth. It should be okay."

When he pulled into the entrance of the Desert Villa Inn, he shook his head in disbelief. "Fran, check the book, are you sure this is the right place?"

The ad's claim that the inn was centrally located between Las Vegas and L.A. was correct. It was also damned near centrally located in the center of highway 40, with not even a lone cactus for landscaping. Two stories with exterior corridors, translated meaning the window view for all rooms was the parking lot and the rooms across the way.

By then, the parking lot was filling with Hell's Angels-type riders with their Harley Hogs.

Reg and I fought through the crowd in the small lobby to the reception desk, where we found a pretty young long-haired blonde so overwhelmed by such a crowd checking in at once, she was almost in tears. When she found our confirmation, she handed us the key to 210 and cautioned, "You'd best go look."

Bless her heart, a wise suggestion. Reg waited in the car while I climbed a time-worn concrete staircase with no guard rails to 210. I opened the door to see a small dark cave decorated in vintage fifties, showing no evidence of the ad's claim of "newly renovated guest rooms."

As I started down those treacherous stairs, four tattooed pony-tailed black-leather Marlon Brando movie "The Wild Ones" bikers were checking into room 110 below room 210. I heard one biker holler, "Hey, Arnie, have we got enough beer for the gang tonight?"

Joining Reg in the car, I said, "We'd get a better night's sleep if we spend the night in our car. You should have let me keep the orange Kawasaki motorcycle I won from buying a lottery ticket from that darling little Boy Scout."

"Fran, you never would have learned to ride that bike, let it go."

Reg returned the key and asked the harried receptionist if there was a penalty for canceling. She waved that question away and was visibly relieved to have a couple of senior citizens leave. I doubt even if we'd arrived on a motorcycle we'd have garnered any respect from this group. I've read that bikers call their wives or girlfriends their "old ladies," but I doubt that a real old lady was what they had in mind.

Next problem. Other than the car, where to sleep? We lucked out with a newly-opened Ramada Inn not listed in my AAA book, so no bikers. We had a super room in the rear, so missed the sound of motorcycles zooming down Main Street all night. Do those men ever sleep?

That evening we had dinner next door at the Cactus Kitchen, and breakfast the next morning on Thursday the 26th. Our waitress was a lovely Japanese woman who endeared herself to me by her kindness to Reg. She made sure he was comfortable and scolded him for not eating enough. When Reg bragged that he was 91, and I had had my 81st birthday the day before, she feigned disbelief and swore on her mother's grave that both of us looked years younger. Never mind, I have no shame and take any compliment gratefully.

234

So Barstow had its good moments. I bought a postcard there picturing a deserted falling-down shack with a For Sale sign, with the words "at last I've found a house in the desert I can afford."

Now came one of the most frightening parts of the trip. We later learned why Barstow was filled with bikers. When we continued on Route 40 for Needles, located on the California-Arizona border, we were surrounded by hundreds of bikers the entire morning. Some passing on the right, some on the left. Since they travel in packs, they would spread out across the narrow road so no one could pass.

Every now and then a biker would lean over to slap his hand on the hood of our car as he whizzed by.

Reg was driving while I was praying. Through clenched teeth, Reg said "Fran, scrunch down, I don't want them to see you. We seem to be the only car traffic on the road—makes me nervous. They are like cockroaches, when I think there are no more, another wave rolls over us."

Just then a biker cut in front so close Reg barely missed him. Reg fumed, "if I'd hit the SOB, it was his fault."

A comment which failed to comfort me. I didn't care whose fault it was if the end result was to die impaled on a cactus bush in the middle of this desolate desert land.

When we stopped in Needles for lunch, we were still puzzled as to why we had an escort of hundreds of bikers from Barstow to Needles. During our lunch at a Denny's restaurant, Reg said, "My guess is a funeral for a fellow biker. I've read that if a Hell's Angel biker dies, his buddies come from all over for the funeral. A few times today I thought it was *our* funeral."

As I was about to agree with him, I glanced at the Arizona Republic newspaper left of our booth. The front page featured photos that solved the mystery. Headline read: "Party time by the River. Bikers head for Laughlin, Nevada. More than 50,000 motorcycle fans are heading to the annual Laughlin River Inn in Laughlin, Nevada on the banks of the Colorado River. The event runs from Wednesday through Sunday and includes hotel discounts, bike exhibits, casino action, and entertainment, including poker runs. Laughlin is 100 miles south of Las Vegas."

After showing the article to Reg, we gave a collective sigh of relief. We could part company with our unwelcome escorts. They were heading north and we were going south for Blythe, California.

Blythe, a small town with a big plus: no bikers. We stayed at the Hampton Inn.

Therefore, since no Blythe resident would invite us for a home-cooked meal, we had two nearby choices: Sizzler's Steak House across the street, and the Kosy Koffee Shop next door. In the 100 degree April heat, neither steak nor hot coffee appealed.

More reconnaissance was needed for this important mission. While Reg took a much-needed nap, I scouted the village for other possibilities.

In the lone Blythe shopping center, Wang's Chinese, a quiet, cool restaurant with its twenty booths, looked inviting, so I made a 7:30pm reservation.

When we arrived at 7:30, Wang's had lost a great deal of charm since afternoon. Instead of the quiet restaurant I had seen then, the place looked as if a children's Headstart Program was in full swing.

THE ARIZONA REPUBLIC

SATURDAY
April 28, 2001 / **SECTION B**

Party time by the river

Photos by Jack Kurtz/The Arizona Republic

Bikers head for Laughlin, Nev.

More than 50,000 motorcycle fans are heading to the 19th annual Laughlin River Run in Laughlin, Nev. The event began Wednesday and runs through Sunday. Tickets are $35 and include a hotel discount, breakfast and entries into drawings. The event includes bike exhibits, casino action, demo rides, poker runs and entertainment, including music concerts and comedian Howie Mandel. Laughlin is 100 miles south of Las Vegas on the banks of the Colorado River. For more information, call (714)-694-2800.

"After showing the article to Reg, we gave a collective sigh of relief. We could part company with our unwelcome escorts."

237

Only one harried petite teenage waitress was visible. While carrying heavy trays down the two aisles, she did her best to avoid several unsupervised pre-schoolers playing leapfrog under her feet.

After fifteen minutes of sitting in the only remaining booth with no attention from the frantic waitress, I said "My mistake, I think we would be doing that dear girl a favor to get out of here."

Bless his heart, Reg agreed and once again, like Barstow when we landed in a newly-opened better hotel, we found a better newly-opened restaurant when we walked across the parking lot into the bright and airy uncrowded Rosita's. Reg said it was the best Mexican food ever.

Next morning we set out for our final destination, Phoenix.

My most vivid memory of our three days in Phoenix was the heat. If it is this hot in the spring, what is it like in the summer? I grew up in Atlanta, Georgia before air conditioning, and we survived our summers there with iced tea, shady trees, and swimming in the few public and private pools. But our Georgia heat was positively arctic compared to this.

Reg spent his days in meetings with the Board members at the Ritz, which was located far from the historic sites such as the Phoenix, Arizona Living History Museum, which replicated the Southwest in the 1880s.

Therefore he thoughtfully arranged for us to stay at the Marriott hotel nearer the things to visit in the way of Phoenix history and its development from a dusty desert Old West front town epitomized by the classic Tom Mix, Gene Autry, and Roy Rogers Saturday afternoon cowboy movies into the sophisticated, vital city it is now.

April 28, the morning after we arrived, I checked the Phoenix map before beginning my walking tour. The blocks from the hotel to the old town are long, and they were not the easy walk to the Arizona State Capitol Museum on Washington Street that I expected. Yet I was determined to reach it. But after several more blocks in the unaccustomed, suffocating heat, my targets, like a desert mirage, looked further away than ever.

When I felt out of breath and dizzy, I was passing a coffee shop that looked open. Maybe water was all I needed…?

When I walked into the welcoming cool, the lull between breakfast and lunch was evident. I climbed up on a stool, lay my head down on the counter, and fainted.

When consciousness returned, I realized a man and woman were taking turns putting cold cloths on my forehead, slapping my wrists while urging me to drink a glass of water. The man asked, "Are you okay? Should we call 911?"

Still groggy but coherent, I assured him I was all right, just needed some water.

It took only one sentence in my southern-accented voice for both people to ask in unison, "What part of the South are you from?"

In a weak voice, I said "Atlanta, Georgia. But now I live in California."

How did I know I had uttered Magic Words? Those two kind people, Irene and Owen Burke, had been born and raised in Atlanta, Georgia.

Sometimes one wonders about coincidences. Of all the restaurants in Phoenix, how did I stumble into one owned by a middle-aged couple from Atlanta? Irene explained that they had owned a coffee shop in College Park near the Atlanta airport for years. Then her asthma had forced them to move to the dry desert climate.

After a long conversation, I said I'd recovered enough to take a cab to the Marriott. Instead, Irene insisted that she had errands that way and drove me back in her pick-up truck.

When Reg returned in the late afternoon, he asked how much of the historic Phoenix buildings I'd seen that day. I said "No, it was too hot to go to museums."

My visit with a couple from my hometown of Atlanta epitomized the spirit of the Old West more than any museum and it was difficult to explain…any more than why we were in Phoenix celebrating a newly-opened chapter to promote Franco-American relationships.

On this earth now, we are all connected one way or another.

In spite of our careful plans to avoid the Los Angeles freeway by taking a longer way to Phoenix, planning our return we decided to take L.A. in case the bikers returned on our previous Needles route.

After Palm Springs, it was my turn to drive. There I was, doing the one thing I dreaded. Reg said "Don't worry Fran, I was living here before I moved to Atlanta. I know the territory, so I'll navigate for you."

So far I had stayed on highway 101, not easy since there are so many difficult decisions with exits every few miles. When we approached several Hollywood exits, Reg yelled "Get over in the right lane. I lived in Hollywood and know lots of good places for lunch."

"Reg, when you were a bachelor there, that was forty years ago. Any place you took all those MGM starlets you dated is gone. Besides, I can't get over to the right lane. These drivers think a turn signal stick is to hang their morning doughnuts on."

Fortunately, even though we were both screaming by then, I had an angel on my shoulder because the red convertible in front of us came to a sudden dead stop. My nightmare had come true. The driver may have been out of gas, had engine trouble, or was having an interesting cell phone conversation. Why, who knew?

I think what saved us is my lifelong habit of using my left foot for brakes and right foot for accelerator rather than moving the right foot back and forth. Reg had scolded me for years on the subject. Personally, I think my immediate brake action saved us—plus the good brakes of the large U-Haul behind us.

Given a choice between the Hell's Angel bikers and the hellish Los Angeles freeway drivers, I'd choose the bikers. I've ordered a t-shirt to read: "I am a survivor of the Los Angeles Freeway System."

We made it to Santa Maria for our last night on the road for our French/Phoenix trip, and assumed that in the middle of the week we'd have no problem staying in our favorite historical Santa Maria inn. To our surprise, a Rodeo Rider's Golf Tournament was in progress, so all the hotels were full. Luckily the registration clerk had a cancellation, so she gave us the last available room.

Maybe the man in the Glen Campbell song "By the Time I Get to Phoenix" had an easier time than we did, in spite of his backward Albuquerque/Oklahoma route after all.

I think we'll stay home from now on.